With the compliments of

C. W. G. Eifrig.

XI. 5, '30.

REPTILES, AMPHIBIANS, AND FISHES

Courtesy *Outdoor America*

A hooked tarpon, or silver king, leaping from the water

OUR GREAT OUTDOORS

REPTILES, AMPHIBIANS, AND FISHES

By
C. W. G. EIFRIG
Instructor in Nature Study,
River Forest, Illinois

RAND McNALLY & COMPANY

NEW YORK   CHICAGO   SAN FRANCISCO

THE ACKNOWLEDGMENTS

The author wishes to make thankful acknowledgment to his many friends who furnished original photographs; to state institutions, scientific societies, museums and their directors and curators, and to publishers: To the Illinois State Natural History Survey, which through its former Nestor and dean, Dr. Stephen A. Forbes[1], granted the privilege to use any or all of the illustrations contained in Forbes and Richardson's monumental work, *The Fishes of Illinois*; to the State Museum of Albany, New York, which through its director, Dr. C. C. Adams, has granted similar favors with respect to certain of the splendid reports of the New York Game and Fish Commission; to the American Museum of Natural History of New York through Dr. Clyde Fisher; to the Boston Society of Natural History and its Dr. Babcock; to the Carnegie Institution of Washington and Dr. Wright; to the New York Zoölogical Society through Dr. Elwin R. Sanborn; to Dr. Thomas Barbour of the Museum of Comparative Zoölogy, Cambridge, Mass.; to the Field Museum of Natural History through its director, Stephen C. Simms; to Doubleday, Doran and Company for permission to reproduce certain pictures from those incomparable volumes in its Nature Library entitled *Reptiles*, by Ditmars, *Frogs*, by Dickerson, and *American Food and Game Fishes*, by Jordan and Evermann, to Quelle and Meyer of Leipzig, Germany, for reproductions from Schmeil's charming *Handbuch der Zoologie*: to the Museum of Natural History of the University of Michigan for a number of photographs; to Mr. W. B. Tyrrell of the Cranbrook Foundation, Birmingham, Mich., for a number of original photographs; similarly to Dr. M. Graham Netting of the Carnegie Museum, Pittsburgh, Pa., and to Mr. A. M. Bailey, director of Academy of Sciences, Chicago.

Especially is he grateful to several of his students who made some of the line drawings, and to his colleague, Professor A. Diesing, who read the manuscript and who wrote one of the appendices.

[1]Recently deceased (March 13, 1930).

A–30

THE CONTENTS

AMPHIBIANS

FISHES

THE INTRODUCTION

Could the brute creation round about us only speak, what a terrible accusation it would make against man as its worst enemy! What great cruelty and heartlessness have been shown innocent animals! If they could but speak, what a pitiful tale they would tell of unmerited persecution and wantonly inflicted pain and death. Just to think of the sufferings men have inflicted on the fur-bearers alone in order to get their furry coats to satisfy human greed and vanity is enough to send a shudder of horror down the spine.

Among the worst sufferers from man's wanton persecution and cruelty are the members of the three classes of vertebrates— reptiles, amphibians, and fishes, especially the reptiles and amphibians. Harmless and even useful as most of them are, they are made to suffer cruelly because of foolish prejudice, dread, and superstition. Many of them, because so easy to kill, have been destroyed in such great numbers that the very existence of some species is threatened. Indeed, in certain sections of their range many varieties have been quite or nearly exterminated.

We pride ourselves on our civilization, on the fact that it is advancing by leaps and bounds, and especially do we pride ourselves on our schools and other educational agencies. But so long as we display in the treatment of the inarticulate fellow inhabitants of our earth a savagery and superstition harking back to the days of the Salem witchcraft, our boast is idle. Let us put an end to this savagery and superstition and become really educated. Let us be humane and sympathetic in our treatment of the dumb creatures of high and low degree around us. Here, of course, I am not referring to our campaigns against the mosquitoes and flies, the cornborer, and similar pests, but to the vertebrates—the mammals, birds, reptiles, amphibians, and fishes—and, in this volume, particularly to the last three

named.   Let us use our schools and all other available agencies
to this end.

What if our outdoors were no longer to know the cheering .
choruses of frogs, the swiftly darting forms of lizards, or the droll,
lumbering figures of the turtles?   Would the destruction of these
creatures really make nature round about us more attractive?
Already we have stilled too many voices by exterminating scores
of useful, or at least harmless, forms of wild life.   Can we today
afford to keep on stilling such voices?

The purpose of this book is not merely to spread knowledge
concerning the animals treated herein, but to instill a sympathetic,
kindly interest in the forms of life surrounding us.   In sheer self-
defense we should make it our business to find out which animals
are harmful and which are harmless to man.   Our well-being
largely depends upon this knowledge.

That this little book may aid in bringing about an intelligent
appreciation of nature is the wish of

THE AUTHOR

REPTILES

A milk snake from New York

A southern milk snake from Maryland

A scarlet king snake from Florida

OUR GREAT OUTDOORS

REPTILES, AMPHIBIANS, FISHES

THE CLASS REPTILES

The word "reptile" is derived from a Latin verb meaning "to creep." Reptiles are creeping vertebrates of greatly varying structure and shape. When snakes, lizards, turtles, and crocodiles—the four orders making up this class—are considered, their great variability as to form and appearance is at once evident. All these species are covered with scales or plates, never with feathers or hair, nor, with a few exceptions, do they have a naked skin as do the amphibians.

The reptiles are cold-blooded, or, more exactly, changeable-blooded vertebrates. This means that the temperature of their blood is not uniform, but varies according to the temperature of the place where they happen to be. If they lie in the sun on a rock or on sand, their blood will be correspondingly warm; if they are in a cool hole in the ground, their blood will be cool. Only when they hibernate during winter, and are buried away underground or even in mud under the water, is their blood really cold. The reason their blood has so little warmth is because their breathing is much slower than that of birds and mammals, although they also breathe through lungs. This slow breathing makes all their life processes more sluggish. We need not be surprised, then, to hear that their blood circulation is sluggish. In fact, the heart of a reptile is not so highly organized as that of birds and mammals, for while the two auricles are separated by a wall, the two ventricles are not entirely divided, thus making an incomplete double circulation. In reptiles the carbon dioxide is never entirely removed, therefore the blood is never entirely cleaned and oxydized.

Accordingly, reptiles are sluggish even in their feeding habits. Just as the blood courses slowly through the veins of a reptile, so also digestion and assimilation are slow. There is not much energy expended in these processes nor is there much waste, and therefore little repair or replenishing is necessary. Some reptiles can get along on astonishingly little food. If a snake has one hearty meal a season, it can live; on one square meal a month, it will thrive; and one meal a week would make it fat. A turtle that I kept in an aquarium would not eat all winter, no matter how much it was tempted.

All reptiles, except turtles, have teeth. Some have teeth even in the palate or roof of the mouth. Their method of propagation is by eggs. The eggs of lizards and snakes are covered by a leathery skin, while those of turtles and crocodiles have a somewhat calcareous or limy shell. Some lizards and snakes are viviparous, that is, they bring forth their young alive.[1]

THE SNAKES

Snakes at once arrest our attention because they have no legs. Instead of the shape of body customary among vertebrates, we see a much elongated cylindrical or wormlike body. In spite of that, snakes can get over the ground, or through water and heavy vegetation, with surprising agility. How is it possible for them to move forward at all?

[1] For internal structure of reptiles, see p. 46.

If you will look at the skeleton of a snake shown on this page you will be astonished at the enormous number of its ribs. Since there is no shoulder girdle, no breastbone or shoulder blade, and no pelvic girdle, each one of these ribs has a free end. These ends serve, in a way, as so many legs. The end of each rib is fastened to a small muscle which, in turn, is attached to one end of the large transverse scales, called *scutes*, on the underside of the snake's body. These scutes are hinged to the body only on the anterior or forward side, the posterior or rear side being free. They are continually raised by pressure from the ribs on those parts of the small muscles attached to each scute. The raised edge of these scutes takes hold of any unevenness of the surface and pulls up on it. Thus, with the additional bending or wriggling of its body from side to side, a snake is able to push itself along or glide

FIG. I.   *The skeleton of a snake*

over the ground quite rapidly. A person lying on the ground makes use of this same principle when he pulls himself up to a projecting stump or rock with his arms. On a smooth surface, such as glass, a snake cannot make headway.

Another peculiarity of the snakes is found in their feeding habits. Perhaps you have seen a small snake in the act of devouring a frog much larger than its head and thicker than the diameter of its body. How can snakes swallow such large objects? One may think that perhaps they slowly chew these to pieces. But this is not so. It is true, as we have already said, that snakes have many teeth in their jaws, and some even on the palate, but these are really only pointed hooks, curved backward, and are used merely for holding their prey, not for chewing it. The teeth are really fangs.

Snakes bolt their food whole. But how can they do this? Because of a very ingenious arrangement of the bones in the head, especially in the jaws. An angular bone, called the *quadrate bone*, connects the upper and the lower jaws of a snake. Because of this bone a snake can extend its mouth up and down to a much greater extent than the size of the head would lead one to believe. Snakes can also extend the lower jaw laterally, since the two halves of the jawbones are not rigidly united in front, but are connected by an elastic band of gristle. Thus they can enlarge the lower jaw until it looks like a large scoop. That snakes can get along with little food has already been stated.

Many snakes are of a dull, uniform color; others are marked with bright colors in attractive patterns. These stripes or figures are formed by the various coloring of the scales. If two or three longitudinal rows of scales have the

same color—for instance, yellow—we have long yellow
stripes, as in the garter snakes.

Most snakes are oviparous, that is, egg-laying. They
lay from six up to sixty or seventy eggs. In some instances
these eggs are nearly as large as a hen's egg, and hatch in
from five to seven weeks. The eggs are usually laid in

After Schmeil

FIG. 2. *Eggs of a snake, with young crawling out*

hollow stumps or in moist, decaying wood, where they absorb
moisture. By the time they are ready to hatch they have
often become almost as large again as when laid.

Quite a number of snakes, however, are viviparous, that
is, they bring forth living young. All the rattlesnakes are
viviparous. Some of them bear as many as sixty or seventy
young at a time. The young often shed their skin an hour
or two after birth, and then every few weeks until fully
grown. After reaching their growth they shed their skin
at least once every season.

It is not only the elongated body of the snakes and the
absence of legs, with the resultant gliding motion, that seem
uncanny to many people, but also the staring look in their
eyes. This effect is due to the absence of eyelids, or rather
to the fact that the lids are grown together in the form of
a transparent membrane. This gives to the eyes that cold,

stony stare that needlessly sends a chill down the spine of so many people.

The split tongue of the snake is not dangerous, as some people believe, for the snake cannot sting with it. The reason snakes move the tongue about so constantly is because it is the seat of their keenest sense, that of touch. Their sight is not keen, nor is their hearing. They have no external ears, but the dark circular spot in the skin behind the eyes is the tympanum or eardrum. The senses of taste and smell are also poorly developed in them.

Snakes spend the winter in hibernating—that is, they crawl into a burrow, or a fissure in the rock, or into some other sheltered place, and become torpid, just as if they were lifeless. We say then that animation is suspended. In summer snakes are fond of basking in the sun. They come from their hiding places among vegetation, or from the water, on to a bare rock or on the sand, and there sun themselves. Then, because they are changeable-blooded, their blood becomes warmed and the life processes are most active.

COMMON NONPOISONOUS SNAKES

THE GARTER SNAKES

Garter snakes. The best known and most common snakes throughout nearly all the United States are the garter snakes. Of these there are nineteen different varieties, ranging from one and a half to two feet in length. / Most of them are black with lengthwise yellow stripes or spots, and some of them therefore are called "ribbon snakes." Garter snakes are viviparous, that is, they bring forth their

Courtesy American Museum of Natura lHistory
Fig. 3. *A garter snake*

young alive, producing as many as fifty to sixty at one time. Since they live only on cold-blooded prey, such as frogs, toads, and worms, they are not really useful. Neither are they so harmful as to warrant the almost universal hatred and loathing in which they are held. In autumn they often gather in numbers on a warm, sunny hillside, preparatory to digging themselves in for the winter. This they do to a depth of a yard or more. One need not be afraid of

Courtesy N. Y. Zoölogical Society

FIG. 4. *A garter snake marked like the one that swallowed the leopard frog*

garter snakes, for they are nonpoisonous and absolutely harmless. One may safely pick them up, for they will not even make an attempt to bite.

The following experience shows how tenacious of life snakes may be. Once, when out in the field with a class of boys, I saw a garter snake that was much distended in the middle of the body. Desiring to learn what the snake had made a meal of, I shot it through the head. It seemed to be as dead as a doornail, and, cutting it open, I found that it contained a large leopard frog. Since the markings of the snake were lines of small, rectangular spots instead of solid yellow lines—a most unusual pattern—I put it into a paper bag and took it home with me. It was not until the second day afterward that I thought of the snake in the bag in the cellar. Wishing to place it in alcohol, I started to open the bag, when all of a sudden the snake glided out and made for a corner in the cellar. Not only was it alive, but it had even kept on developing in its usual way, the lines of interrupted yellow spots having in those two days become uninterrupted yellow lines. Now, does not that beat the proverbial nine lives of a cat!

THE WATER SNAKES

Water snakes in the United States. The brown or black-ish snakes so often found sunning themselves on logs in rivers and swamps belong to the species of water snake, of which thirteen different varieties are found in the United

Courtesy N. Y. Zoölogical Society

FIG. 5.   *The water snake*

States. This is another viviparous species, bringing forth as many as forty-four young in a season. The young are rather attractively marked and colored, being covered with small square spots of brown or of maroon and white. As these snakes become older this pattern fades or becomes covered by the dust and dirt in their muddy habitat. Since the food of the water snake consists of fishes and frogs, it lives in rivers and swamps or near them. It is often called "moccasin" or "water moccasin," but this name belongs properly to the poisonous species of that name found in the South which is also called "cottonmouth." The water snake has a vicious temper and sometimes strikes

FIG. 6.   *The smaller of these snakes is the De Kay's snake*

on slight provocation, but it is not poisonous.   It attains
a large size, frequently reaching forty-two inches in length.
In some swamps there are so many of these water snakes
that they become a great pest and could well stand some
thinning out.

Once when wading through a river in Indiana I saw a
water snake swimming ahead of me.   It could not move
very readily, for it had a six-inch catfish in its mouth.
The catfish was struggling with all its might, but could not
free itself from the sharp teeth of the snake.   Taking pity
on the poor catfish, I killed the snake, as I thought, whereupon the fish swam away, no doubt congratulating itself on
its narrow escape.   I stretched out the snake on a log that
lay half in the river and half on the shore.   When I returned
that way an hour or two later and stepped on the log, the
snake seemed suddenly to awaken as from a deep sleep and
plunged into the river as though it had not been "killed"
an hour before.

THE BROWN SNAKES

De Kay's snake. Sometimes in September one finds a little brown snake crawling across the way. It is called *De Kay's snake*, also *brown* or *ground snake*. The name De Kay has been given to it in honor of the naturalist of that name who lived in New York about a hundred years ago. This snake is usually from eight to twelve inches long and is perfectly harmless and gentle. In fact it is useful, since it lives entirely on insects. It is viviparous, giving birth to from twelve to twenty young.

Another tiny species of the brown snake, and a close relative of the De Kay, is the little *red-bellied* or *Storer's snake*. It is brown above and bright red below, but otherwise it is just like the brown snake.

THE BLACK SNAKE

The racers. The black snake, also called the *black racer*, is commonly found throughout eastern North America. The so-called *blue racer* is only a color variety of the black. The name "racer" is properly applied because the speed with which these snakes can get over the ground is almost unbelievable.

The early pioneers in our central states claimed to have seen black snakes eight and ten feet long and even longer. I see no reason to doubt their statements, because, except for the few killed by natural enemies and by the Indians, the snakes had lived undisturbed for ages in the lush river and creek bottoms. Even now, when everyone's hand is against them, black snakes seven feet long are occasionally found.

Stories telling that they sometimes approach a person, their head held high up in the air, intending to pick a fight

2

or else wind themselves around his legs, are all buncombe, or fairy tales, and as unworthy of belief in our matter-of-fact age as is the story that the black snake makes it its

FIG. 7. *A black snake hanging from a tree*

chief business in life to attack every rattlesnake it meets. Neither does the black snake charm chipmunks and birds with a hypnotic stare of its eyes. But when cornered it will put up a fight that does credit to its courage. The black snake is even useful, inasmuch as it destroys rats, mice, and other rodents found around and under buildings as well as in the fields. It is not a constrictor, that is, it does not kill by winding itself around its victim and crushing it. Instead, because of its great speed, it catches its prey, then holds it down with its weight, and starts to swallow it.

FIG. 8. *A black snake in characteristic coils on the ground*

During June or July the black snake lays from one to two dozen eggs under a flat stone or in soft, moist soil. The eggs at first are snowy white, but are rough, as though they had been sprinkled with salt. It takes six or seven weeks for them to hatch, and during that time they have swelled to a length of two inches. At first the young snakes are

quite different from the old in color, being pale gray above
with large round spots and whitish on the sides; the abdomen
is also pale gray.   Not until the third year do the snakes
become shiny black like the adults.

The *coachwhip snake*, the southern representative of the
black snake, is even longer and more slender than its northern relative.   It reaches a length of eight feet, the long tail

FIG. 9.   *The coachwhip snake*

being almost as thin as the end of a whip.   This snake is
almost entirely black, becoming brownish or grayish toward
the tail.   Some coachwhip snakes are even reddish or
greenish in color.

West of the Mississippi River there is a variety of the
black snake called the *blue racer*.   This differs from the
blue racer found east of the Mississippi in being bluish-
green or even olive above, with the abdomen a pale yellow.
I have found, however, a very light greenish-blue one
in the Indiana sand dunes on the south shore of Lake
Michigan.

The *indigo snake* of the southeastern states of the Union
is a rather handsome species, glittering blue-black in color.

It is also the largest snake in the eastern United States, reaching a length of nine feet. Since it is often seen gliding into the holes of the large gopher turtle, which lives in the

Photograph by W. Bryant Tyrrell

FIG. 10.   *The blue racer*

FIG. 11.   *The fox snake*

same region, it is also called "gopher snake." It makes itself useful by catching the several kinds of rats found on farms and plantations in the South. Its eggs are as large as those of a bantam chicken.

THE RAT SNAKES OR COLUBERS

The fox snake. The fox snake is so called because, when excited, it will eject from glands at the base of the tail an evil-smelling secretion. This has about the same odor as that noticed about the den or cage of a fox. Many snakes, even the common garter snake, have such scent glands. The fox snake is a rather good-natured snake, despite the sneeze-like hiss it emits. It is useful to the farmer, because its food consists solely of rodents or gnawing mammals which, if unchecked, would soon endanger or destroy all crops. It is pale brown or yellowish in color, with rich brown splotches on the back and smaller ones on the sides. It is a handsome fellow and a true constrictor, for it crushes and kills its prey by winding its strong, lithe body around it and then drawing the loops tightly together. The female lays her dozen or two of eggs in rotting stumps, where they hatch in from six to eight weeks.

A relative of the fox snake is the *corn* or *mouse snake* (also called *red chicken snake, scarlet racer*, and *house snake*) found from Maryland south and southwest. It is a beautiful snake, having a pale red ground color, with large crimson spots or "saddles" on its back. Below, it is white with large black squares, a pattern also shown by other species, as for

Courtesy American Museum of Natural History

FIG. 12.   *A young chicken snake*

instance the milk snake. When seen in cornfields the corn snake is out after mice and rats and is therefore useful to man. It will, however, eat birds, even climbing trees after them.

The pilot snake. The pilot snake, another member of the constrictor family, attains a length of five feet, and is often mistaken for the black snake. It is called "pilot" snake because it is supposed to warn rattlesnakes and copperheads of danger and to lead them into safety. That, of course, is a superstition; but it is true that this snake is found on rocky ledges and in other places where these poisonous species like to bask. The pilot snake is found from Massachusetts

Courtesy American Museum of Natural History
FIG. 13.   *The pilot snake*

to Illinois and Florida. It is fond of chickens and their eggs; it is therefore also called *black chicken snake*.

Among these strong-bodied constrictors we ought to mention the *banded chicken snake, yellow chicken snake*, or *yellow rat snake*. This is a large yellow snake with four brown or black stripes, two on the back and one on each side. It reaches a length of six or seven feet. It ranges through our southeastern states west to the Mississippi. Often it is found in trees twenty feet or more from the ground. That the birds do not welcome this peculiar visitor is certain. This snake is fond of chicken eggs, which it swallows and crushes inside its body. It also devours rats and thus makes itself useful.

The pine or bull snake. The *pine, bull*, or *white gopher snake*—the eastern member of this group—is found from the New Jersey pine barrens south to Florida and west to Ohio. In color it is whitish, with chestnut-brown blotches which are margined with black, besides three more lines of spots. It is a large, heavy-bodied snake, sometimes reaching a length of eight feet, its usual size, however, being about four feet. It is a constrictor but a good-natured snake, and although it is powerful enough to kill such animals as woodchucks or medium-sized dogs, it confines itself to small mammals, such as rabbits, squirrels, and rats. It is also fond of birds and their eggs and makes nothing of swallowing six chicken eggs. R. L. Ditmars, the curator of reptiles in the Zoölogical Garden at New York, tells of one bull snake to which he fed fourteen chicken eggs at one time, and the only reason it did not eat more was because there were no more. The snake swallows the eggs whole, but when they are down a foot or so they are broken by a constriction of the muscles of that part of the body.

While touring in western South Dakota several years ago I saw many of these snakes lying dead across the road. They had been run over by automobiles. This was the *bull* or *yellow gopher snake*, the word "pine" not being given to this species when found between the Mississippi River and the Rockies. It is chestnut brown in color, with many orange cross marks and spots; the sides are mottled with black and orange. Still farther west, from southern Oregon to Arizona and western Texas, the *Arizona bull snake* is found, and west of the Sierras the *Pacific bull snake*.

All these bull snakes lay from fifteen to twenty-five eggs which are the size of a hen's eggs.

THE GREEN SNAKE

The green or grass snake. The green or grass snake is a small, dainty serpent, which, true to its name, is green. This is protective coloration, as the snake lives among the leaves in bushes and small trees. It subsists on spiders,

caterpillars, grasshoppers, and other insects and is therefore a useful little snake and should never be killed. The
green snake is very gentle, allowing itself to be taken up
and handled without showing anger or making any attempt
to bite. Sometimes it grows to be two feet long, but usually
it is only from ten to fifteen inches in length. The green
snake is found from southern Canada to the Gulf of Mexico.

Courtesy N. Y. Zoölogical Society

FIG. 14.   *The king snake*

The eggs are laid under flat stones. There are several
species of green snake in the various parts of the country.

THE RING-NECKED SNAKES

Ring-necked snakes. As the name would indicate, the
ring-necked snakes, of which there are three species, can
easily be distinguished by the bright yellow ring just below
the head. Except for this ring they are black or gray above
and yellow below, while the underside of the tail is a
bright coral red. The eastern ring-necked snake has a wide

range, extending from southern Canada to the Gulf and west to the Mississippi. Yet this snake is rarely seen for the reason that it is very secretive, hiding itself away under such things as loose bark and stones. It is about the same size as the green snake.

THE KING SNAKES

King snakes. The members of this family, seven in number in the United States, are fine, well-built, strong

Courtesy N. Y. Zoölogical Society

FIG. 15. *A milk snake*

snakes, usually striking in color. They should be protected by everyone, especially the farmer, because they prey upon the mice, rats, and other rodents which make such costly inroads on his crops. In addition to this usefulness they have a decided liking for snake meat, and so kill and devour many other snakes, large and small, young and old, poisonous and nonpoisonous.

The *milk* or *house snake* is a member of the king snake family. This snake suffers because of the foolish prejudice of many people. Since it is often found in stables near cows, or in cellars where milk is kept, the belief has gained ground that it is so fond of milk that it either milks the cows or else drinks the milk from the crocks in the spring house or cellar. As a matter of fact, this snake when in captivity cannot be induced to drink milk. The truth is, it is found in such places because that is where it can find its

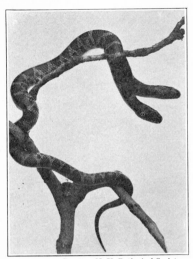

Courtesy N. Y. Zoölogical Society

FIG. 16. *A two-headed milk snake in a tree*

favorite food, mice and rats. In the stomach of one milk snake were found five very young rats. Like other members of this species, it also kills and eats other snakes. Why kill such an ally and friend? A desire to kill every snake one sees shows a lack of judgment and of common sense. The milk snake is rather handsome, being gray above, with a number of large, chestnut-brown, saddle-shape spots, while below it is white, with irregular black spots and rectangles.[1] As a rule it lays from eight to twelve eggs, from which the young snakes emerge after about seven weeks.

The *king, chain,* or *thunder snake* is another useful and handsome member of this family. It is usually black, with narrow yellow or white crossbands which connect with one another on the sides and have given it the name of "chain snake." Some of these snakes are a beautiful red or scarlet, with yellow and black rings around the body. The scales of the back are glossy and polished, while those of the abdomen are glassy and lustrous, giving it a fine appearance. It grows to a length of six feet. This length, however, is

[1] See colored plate opposite p. 3.

reached by snakes only in the South, where all snakes are larger than the same or related kinds in the North.

The king snake gets its name from the fact that it seems to lord it over all other snakes, even over many that are larger than itself. It will attack and fight most snakes, crushing the life out of them by the constriction of its strong body and then devouring them. While its chief outdoor sport is not hunting for rattlesnakes, as some people believe, it will at once attack any rattlesnake it happens to meet, and hold it with its constriction. Naturally the rattlesnake or copperhead or moccasin will strike it again and again, but without making any impression on the king snake, for it is *entirely immune to snake poison.*

The king snake gives off a powerful musky odor from a gland near the base of the tail. The female deposits from ten to twenty-four eggs, which require from five to six weeks for hatching.

THE HOG-NOSED SNAKE OR BLOWING VIPER

The hog-nosed snake. One of the most misunderstood and maligned snakes is the hog-nosed snake, also known as *spreading adder, puff adder, blowing viper, flat-headed adder, blow snake, land viper,* and *hoop snake.* The number of its names shows that it is well known and is found over a large area, while the kinds of names show some of its characteristics. And it is these characteristics that have brought this harmless snake into bad repute. It is a thick, short snake that cannot get up enough speed to reach cover when found basking on bare sand, its favorite place. When one suddenly comes upon it, the snake will draw in as much air as it can and blow itself up. First its head and neck, and finally its whole body will flatten out, so that it becomes three times its normal width. Then indeed does it look formidable and dangerous. This effect is heightened by the hissing sound it makes, as some of its names indicate.

People are convinced by its hissing that the hog-nosed snake must be deadly poisonous and will resent having anyone try to shake this conviction.

In spite of all this, the hog-nosed snake is really harmless. When acting its worst it will refuse to bite, and even if it did bite it could do no harm, for it has no poison glands or fangs. Despite its apparent ferocity, it is a harmless and gentle creature. When sorely pressed, the hog-nosed snake will suddenly flop over on its back and feign death. And if turned back on its belly it will immediately turn over on its back again, as though this absurd action on its part would force the beholder to believe it dead.

FIG. 17. *The common hog-nosed snake*

There are three varieties of the hog-nosed snake in the United States, one in the eastern, one in the southern, and one in the western section of the country.

The color of the puff adder is as follows. The ground color is a pale yellowish brown, with about thirty-five darker blotches on the back. In some cases these markings are brick red; in others, the whole snake seems nearly black.

The food of the blowing viper is toads and frogs.

Now, what about the famous "hoop snake"? This is none other than the hog-nosed snake, the species we have just been discussing. In the Southeast this name is given to the *rainbow snake*, a brilliantly colored burrowing species.

Now and then one will hear some person say that he has seen a snake take its tail in its mouth and roll downhill in the form of a hoop. And apparently he thinks he is telling the truth. Is the story true or not? I, for my part, should be unwilling to believe it unless I saw such a thing with my own eyes. A person sometimes dreams something so vividly that a few days later he does not know whether or not he actually had such an experience. An old man known for his shrewdness, who had lived most of his life in the country, once told me that he had seen a snake roll down a hill in hoop fashion, unwind at the bottom, and *with its tail* strike a cherry tree, which immediately died! And he almost became angry with me when I smiled incredulously at him! Let us rid ourselves of belief in such silly superstitions and fairy tales!

FIG. 18.   *The reticulated python of Malaya*

One of the largest snakes in the world.   This half-grown specimen is about
ten feet long.

NONPOISONOUS SNAKES OF OTHER COUNTRIES

THE PYTHONS

The best known nonpoisonous snakes outside of North America are the huge pythons of the tropics, such as the *boa constrictor* and *anaconda* of South America, and similar snakes in Asia and Africa.

After Brehm

FIG. 19. *The boa constrictor*

After Brehm

FIG. 20.   *The anaconda in its native habitat*

54356

The boa attains a length of from twelve to fourteen feet. Its markings are rather attractive—a light brown, with dark bars and spots. Young boas are sometimes brought into the United States in bunches of bananas. In its home in the jungles of South America the boa often lies on low branches of trees and from there, holding on to its support with its prehensile tail, it falls on its prey, such as tapirs, capybaras, young deer, and smaller animals which may be passing beneath. It kills its prey by constriction, winding itself around the body of its victim and then drawing its coils together, thus crushing the animal into a shapeless mass. Then the huge serpent will cover this mass with its saliva to make it slippery enough so that it may be swallowed easily. After such a heavy meal the great snake will be in a semi-torpid condition, hardly able to move. Now it may be approached and killed quite easily.

The *anaconda*, a boa living in or near the water, is said to reach a length of forty feet. If, however, there are anacondas of this size, they must be rare indeed. The anaconda is able to stay under water a long time, and often does so, making fish its main food. Frequently it lets itself drift along with the current of the river, its head extended above the water, while it looks around for prey on shore. What a terror it must strike into a tapir, or agouti, or even a duck or heron, to find itself suddenly confronted by this monster snake! As a rule the anaconda lets man alone, but there are cases on record which show that it occasionally deviates from this rule.

The Indian python is said to attain a length of thirty feet, its spinal column having as many as four hundred vertebrae. The African python reaches a length of twenty feet, but most of those seen are from ten to fifteen feet long.

3

Roosevelt, in his book *African Game Trails*, tells us that once during his journey in Africa he went swimming on a hot day in an inviting looking pool. Suddenly he noticed that a ten-foot python was also using the same pool to cool itself off, whereupon Mr. Roosevelt made a bee line for the shore.

THE POISONOUS SNAKES

All the snakes discussed thus far are harmless, in some instances even beneficial to man. This is not true of poisonous snakes. These snakes carry with them a terrible weapon—their poison—fatal alike to man and beast. It is therefore desirable that we learn to distinguish by sight the dangerous snakes from the harmless ones.

Courtesy N. Y. Zoölogical Society

FIG. 21. *The rhinoceros viper, or river jack, of West Africa*
This is one of the most venomous of snakes.

Our poisonous snakes, with the exception of the small coral snake in Texas, can all be distinguished from the harmless ones by the fact that the head is triangular and much broader than the body, whereas the head of a non-poisonous snake is little, if any, broader than its neck and body. The tail of the poisonous species is short and thick and the body heavy, making these snakes appear shorter and thicker than they really are.   Finally, all our poisonous snakes—again with the exception of the coral snake—have a deep pit between the eye and nostril.   This pit, however, cannot be seen at a distance.

Because of their heavy, thick body, poisonous snakes cannot catch their prey as easily as can the more agile ones. They must have other means to secure their prey, and their poison apparatus serves this purpose.   No snake is poisonous—no matter how sinister its appearance or how

Courtesy N. Y. Zoölogical Society

FIG. 22.   *The jararaca of South America, a relative of the bushmaster*

closely its color and pattern resemble that of a poisonous species, and no matter how earnestly people may affirm its harmfulness—unless it has poison glands and fangs. Behind and below each eye is a poison gland, a small sac, in which the poison is manufactured.   From each gland a small tube or duct leads into a poison fang.   The fang is a hollow tooth fixed on a movable bone in the roof of the mouth.   The fangs are not movable, but the bone on which they are set is movable.

When an animal, such as a mouse or a rabbit or a frog, has come close enough to a poisonous snake, the snake will dart forward its head, at the same time opening its jaws. Its fangs, which at other times are folded back against the palate in a sheath of white flesh, are thereby erected so that they point nearly straight forward. This motion is usually so quick that the eye cannot follow it. The snake really *stabs* the victim with the poison fangs rather than bites it. As the jaws close, the muscles contract and press against the poison gland. In this way the poison is forced through the duct and canal in the tooth, and through the

Courtesy N. Y. Zoölogical Society

FIG. 23. *The urutu of Brazil*
A poisonous species of South America, also a relative of the bushmaster.

opening at the end of the fang, into the wound. If the victim is a frog or a mouse with a small, round body, the snake will, of course, close the mouth over a part of the body and thus bite and inject the poison. Even this is done so rapidly that it is scarcely perceptible. The small animal becomes paralyzed and in a minute or two will succumb to the poison. Then the snake, by means of its distensible jaws, swallows the body of its prey.

The poison fangs are shed about every three months, often being left imbedded in the body of a victim. But

before they are shed, a new fang has already begun to grow
beside the old one and to connect itself with the poison
gland.

From what distance can a snake strike with any degree
of accuracy? Only about one-half of its own length. Sometimes a badly frightened or an angered snake will strike at
a distance equal to two-thirds of its length, but such blows
are wild and aimless. No poisonous snake ever springs
bodily at its victim, whether man or animal.

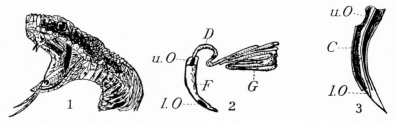

After Schmeil

FIG. 24. *Head and poison apparatus of a venomous serpent*

1, head with open mouth, showing poison fangs extended and other fangs
partly formed; 2, poison apparatus; 3, poison fang, cut through vertically; *G*,
poison gland; *D*, duct into the fang; *F*, fang; *u. O*, upper and *l. O*, lower opening
of poison canal, *C*.

What must one do if bitten by a poisonous snake? First,
shut off the flow of blood from the bitten member by tying
a ligature above the wound. A handkerchief tied firmly
around the limb and tightened by being twisted with an
inserted stick will do. Then with a knife or some other
sharp instrument enlarge the wound by cutting into the
flesh as deep at least as the fangs went. This is done to
cause a flow of blood which will wash out the poison. Sucking out the blood from the wound is effective, but must not
be done if one has a sore in the mouth or on the lip, or
a hollow tooth. The wound should be washed out with a

solution of permanganate of potassium, if that can be obtained. But send for a good doctor at once or go to one yourself as quickly as possible after these first measures have been taken.

THE RATTLESNAKES

There are only four kinds of poisonous snakes in the United States or in all North America north of the Rio Grande—the rattlesnakes, the water moccasin, the copperhead, and the coral snake.

Rattlesnakes. There are about a dozen species of rattlesnakes, most of them being found in our southern and southwestern states. Only the *Pacific rattler*, the *prairie rattler*, and the *massasauga* extend their range northward into Canada, and then not very far. It is in the South that we find the greatest

From *Lizards and Snakes of North America*, by Edward Drinker Cope

FIG. 25. *The prairie rattlesnake*

variety of reptiles, both poisonous and nonpoisonous. Since the blood temperature of reptiles varies with the temperature of the air, they naturally feel life pulsating more strongly through their bodies in the warm Southland, and there their life activities, including reproduction, are greater than in the cooler North.

It is in warm, dry, sunny places, too, that the rattlesnake likes to live and bask. Then it is not looking for trouble, nor is it even desiring food, since it can get along on very little food, especially in the cool North.   One square meal a month is enough, and it can get along on even less than that if need be.

The rattlesnake may be called the gentleman among snakes, for when a person comes too close it gives him fair warning.   This it does by means of the rattle or buzzer at the end of its tail. Any snake, however, when excited or angered, may vibrate its tail, and if this happens among dead leaves it will cause a sound like the rattle of the rattlesnake. Because of the fair warning given by the rattlesnake, few people are bitten.   It will crawl away before one sees it, rather than fight.

From *Lizards and Snakes of North America*, by Edward Drinker Cope
FIG. 26.   *The diamond-back rattlesnake*

Courtesy N. Y. Zoölogica Society
FIG. 27.   *The horned rattlesnake*

All species of rattlesnakes are viviparous, the female giving birth to from seven to a dozen young.   They shed their skin soon after birth, showing at the end of the tail a button which is the beginning of the rattle.   In later molts the rattle is not shed along with the skin.   It is impossible to tell exactly the age of a rattlesnake by counting the number of rings in the rattle.   The snake may produce two, three, or even four

Photograph by Elwin R. Sanborn; courtesy N. Y. Zoölogical Society

FIG. 28.   *The massasauga*

rings in a single year.   But when ten or eleven rings are on its tail it seldom gets more, because the vibration is so strong that any additional rattles are soon broken or worn off.

The only rattlesnake in the eastern United States is the *timber* or *banded rattlesnake (Crotalus horridus)*.   Farther west are found the *prairie rattlesnake (C. confluentus)* and the *massasauga (Sistrurus catenatus)*, their range extending into southern Canada.   In the western mountain and plateau region occurs the *Pacific rattlesnake (C. oregonus)*, which is also found in British Columbia.

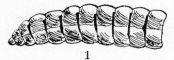   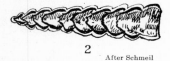

1   2

After Schmeil

FIG. 29.   *Rattle of rattlesnake*

1, seen from above; 2, cut through longitudinally.

The most dangerous species is the southern *diamond-back rattlesnake*, so called from the markings on its back.

FIG. 30.   *The copperhead*

It reaches a length of more than eight feet, and will not always get out of man's way, but sometimes attacks him. It is an extremely dangerous snake.

THE COPPERHEAD

The copperhead. This short, thick, sluggish snake is usually about three feet long.   It lives in hilly regions from Massachusetts to Florida, west to Missouri, where the sunny knobs of the Ozarks are much to its liking, and southwest to Texas.   Warm, rocky places, sunny, brush-covered hillsides, old quarries, and little swampy ravines are the places where this snake likes to stay.   Often it hibernates in the deep clefts of a quarry.   In color it is hazel-brown, with large crossbands of rich chestnut brown.

Courtesy A. M. Bailey

FIG. 31.   *The water moccasin or cottonmouth*
Note the white inside its mouth.

It is said to emit an odor like that of green cucumbers freshly sliced. The copperhead, evidently believing discretion to be the better part of valor, glides away when danger in the shape of man approaches. Injury or death from its bite is therefore rare. It is viviparous, giving birth to from six to nine young.

THE WATER MOCCASIN

The water moccasin. The water moccasin, or *cottonmouth*, lives in the southern states, in wet, swampy places. The name "cottonmouth" is given to it because of the peculiar white skin in the inside of its mouth. In color it is a dull olive or dark brown, with indistinct black markings. The moccasin lies lazily on logs in swamps such as the Everglades in Florida, basking in the sun, and hurriedly slipping off when a human being approaches. Its food consists of fish, frogs, and other snakes. Its thick, sluggish body reaches a length of four feet and more. It is one of the commonest snakes of the South, every pond and pool harboring numbers of them. In one prairie pond near Houston, Texas, that we waded around in for hours, the owner's son had caught forty-two of this species in a barrel the preced-

FIG. 32.   *The coral snake*

ing week—and, as we noticed, he did not get them all. In spite of this abundance one relatively rarely hears of people being bitten by the cotton-mouth, although young and old wade about unconcernedly in waters infested with this reptile. It seems too sluggish and lazy to bite. The com-mon water snake of the north-ern states, sometimes called "water moccasin," is an entirely different, nonpoisonous species.

All the poisonous snakes we have discussed are immune to their own poison. They can and sometimes do strike one another without fatal results.

THE CORAL SNAKE

The coral snake. The pretty little *coral* or *harlequin snake*, the last poisonous snake north of the Rio Grande to be discussed, ranges from the Carolinas to Texas. It is quite different in appearance from the viperine snakes or pit vipers we have just considered, for it is slender, graceful, and highly colored. Its markings consist of broad rings of deep scarlet and blue-black, separated by narrow rings of yellow. Usually it is from two to two and a half feet long. The head is no thicker than the neck or body. The poison of the coral snake, however, is extremely virulent; in fact, this little snake is a relative of the deadly cobra of India.

But luckily its mouth is so small that it cannot open it wide enough to seize any portion of man's anatomy. Therefore deaths from its bite are very rare indeed, one occurring perhaps once in many years. Besides, this snake is very timid and small and is also secretive, staying in the ground most of the time. The food of the coral snake consists of lizards and small snakes. It is oviparous, depositing about seven eggs in damp soil or in decaying bark.

POISONOUS SNAKES OF OTHER COUNTRIES

In Mexico, Central America, the West Indies, and tropical South America is found the deadly *bushmaster*, a forest-

loving species twelve feet long. Its bite is almost without exception fatal. A relative of this snake, the dreaded *fer-de-lance* or *lance-head*, or the *palm viper*, is found lurking in the dense undergrowth and is quite dangerous.

Europe has few poisonous snakes. The *cross viper* or *Kreuzotter* is the only one found over large parts of the continent. It gets its name from the crosslike markings on the head.

After Brehm

FIG. 33. *The dangerous bushmaster*

THE COBRA

The *cobra-de-capello* of India is a dangerous reptile and to its poison ten to twenty thousand people succumb each year. It can flatten out its neck until it takes on the shape of a round flat hat. The cobra, therefore, is also called "hat snake." This is the snake the Indian fakirs carry about in baskets and which with their droning, monotonous music they hypnotize into a state of harmlessness.

Some of these fakirs remove all danger to themselves by extracting the poison fangs of their snakes from time to time, but most of them scorn this precaution and deception

From *Lizards and Snakes of North America*, by Edward Drinker Cope

FIG. 34.   *The West Indian fer-de-lance*

and for a few pennies risk the danger of being bitten by these deadly serpents.

In his book *The Last Home of Mystery*, E. A. Powell states that the snake charmers excite the cobras in the morning, and have them strike several times through heavy cloth until the poison is exhausted.   That practice perhaps explains why these men so rarely die of the bite of their poisonous snakes.

The common cobra is from six to seven feet long, but the terrible *king cobra*, or *hamadryad*, reaches a length of from twelve to eighteen feet.   Often it refuses to go out of man's way and even attacks him.   This snake is greatly feared by the natives of India, Burma, and Siam, and annually many natives die from the bite of this dreaded reptile.

Scarcely less destructive of life is the *krait* of India.   It attains a length of four to six feet and is beautifully marked with blue-black and yellow bands of equal width.

Another species of cobra is the notorious *spitting snake* of Africa, which readily turns on a pursuer or will even attack first. This snake gets its name from its habit of spitting or throwing its venom a number of feet, usually aiming at the eyes of an opponent. If the poisonous fluid reaches its mark, it causes such violent pain as to render the victim almost helpless, and it is a number of days before the normal sight of the eyes is restored.

From *Lizards and Snakes of North America*, by Edward Drinker Cope

FIG. 35. *An Indian cobra*

THE LIZARDS

One can see at a glance that the lizards must be close relatives of the snakes. There is the same elongated shape, the same forked tongue, and scales much like those of snakes. The tail in many lizards is very long and gently tapering. For instance, the six-lined lizard may be ten

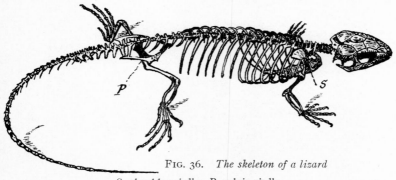

FIG. 36. *The skeleton of a lizard*

S, shoulder girdle; *P,* pelvic girdle

inches long, seven inches of which is tail. The tail of this and other lizards is brittle, a peculiarity not possessed in the same degree by snakes. If one takes hold of a lizard by the tail, in an instant he will find himself holding only a twitching tail, the reptile itself having fled. A second tail will grow out, but it will not be as long as the first one.

There are also, of course, a number of other important differences between lizards and snakes. Nearly all lizards have four legs. One or two species have only two legs, and one, the glass snake, none at all—at least not externally. Their skeleton, therefore, shows the shoulder girdle, where the forelegs are fastened, and the pelvic girdle, where

4

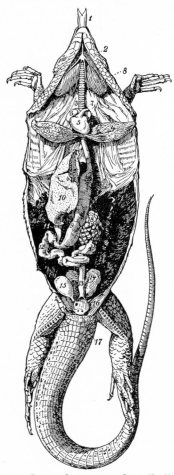

Fig. 37.   *Internal structure of reptile (lizard)*

1, tongue; 2, hyoid bone; 3, windpipe; 4, lung, turned aside; 5, ventricle of heart; 6, right auricle of heart; 7, large artery; 8, lower jaw, with masticator muscle; 9, stomach; 10, liver; 11, pancreas; 12, small intestine; 13, end of intestine; 14, kidney; 15, bladder; 16, cloaca; 17, vent; 18, ovary.

the hind legs are inserted. The legs end in five digits, furnished with claws. Many lizards can move their legs with such extraordinary rapidity that the eye can hardly follow

FIG. 38. *Head of lizard*
Note the forked tongue, the organ in reptiles for the sense of touch.

After Schmeil

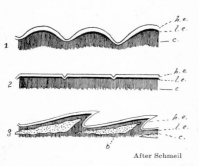

After Schmeil

FIG. 39. *Skin of reptiles*
1, granulations; 2, plates; 3, scales, or skin (in the cutis of 3 are shown bony plates, *b*, imbedded in the cutis); *h. e.*, horny epidermis; *l. e.*, living epidermis; *c.*, cutis, or lower skin.

them. This is also true of their movements in catching insects. Several kinds of lizards have a habit of rearing up on their hind legs and then running with the same swiftness.

Lizards have a large mouth. It runs "from ear to ear," but is not dilatable. The jaws are furnished with a row of small, conical teeth. Just a little back of the corners of the mouth are the ears, visible only as round tympanic membranes, just as in snakes and frogs.

The colors shown by lizards are most often those of their surroundings, grays and browns like sand and the bark of trees. Some have bright yellow lines running lengthwise over the body, and a region of beautiful blue or violet around the hind legs, on the sides of the body, and on the tail. There is a great variability in the color of lizards, not only among individuals of the same species but even from time

FIG. 40. *A chuckawalla lizard*

FIG. 41. *Spike-tailed lizards*

to time in the same individual. Some change greatly in appearance when old. Many are even able to change their color at short notice, the best known of these lizards being the chameleon.

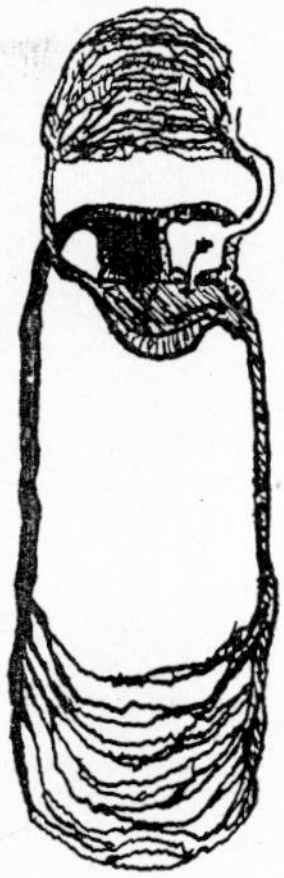

The propagation of the lizard varies with the groups. Most lizards lay their eggs in sand or in damp vegetation, such as moss or rotting wood. These eggs hatch in from six to eight weeks. Other lizards produce living young, surrounded by a thin membrane through which the young break an hour or two after birth. A third group, the horned lizards or toads, like certain of the snakes, produces living young without membrane or shell.

A FEW OF OUR COMMON LIZARDS

We know how fond snakes are of lying in the sun, but lizards, even more than snakes, are creatures of the sun, often basking in its heat for hours at a time. There are fewer lizards than snakes found in our northern states, and in Canada there are next to none. The greatest variety of lizards north of the Rio Grande is found in the southwestern states. Where we find one or two species in the northern states, we find a score of species in the sandy or rocky deserts of western Texas, New Mexico, and Arizona. It is to the tropics, however, that we must turn for the greatest development of lizards in respect to size, shape, and numbers.

Six-lined lizard. The only species found near Chicago is the six-lined lizard, so called from the six narrow yellow lines running down over its body. It is found among the sand

FIG. 42. *Heart and blood circulation of lizard* Notice the unseparated ventricles.

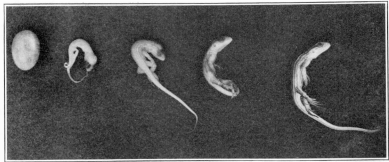

Courtesy N. Y. Zoölogical Society
FIG. 43.   *Development of the six-lined lizard*

dunes of northwestern Indiana.   So swift are its movements
that it is next to impossible to catch one.   This lizard grows
to be nine or ten inches in length, more than two-thirds
of which is tail.   It is a trim, neat looking creature and,
needless to say, is entirely harmless.   It is found from Connecticut and Wisconsin southwest to Mexico.

Blue-tailed lizard.   In southern Illinois and southward is
found the blue-tailed lizard, dark olive in color, with five
yellowish streaks and a bright blue tail.   The head of an
old one becomes coppery red and the stripes disappear.
In fact, the color of these lizards is so changeable that it is
now supposed by some that the blue-tailed lizard is nothing
but the young stage of the five-lined skink.   The blue-
tailed lizard, as well as several other species, may be found
in and on the bark of tree trunks as often as on the ground.

The chameleon.   In pine woods from Tennessee to
Florida and south to Cuba and Mexico is found the chameleon, so called after the famous Old World chameleon,
which is known for its ability to change its color at will.
This is done not so much to make the color match that of
its surroundings as from fear, anger, sleepiness, change of

FIG. 45. *An iguana, called dragon in Mexico. See page 55*

FIG. 44. *A chameleon*

temperature, or some similar cause. It will then change, say from brown to bright green, in three minutes. The means by which this is accomplished seems to be a change in the position of the epidermal cell walls or partitions,

FIG. 46. *The common swift*

which in their varying positions reflect the various colors contained ·in the sun's light. The chameleon when fully grown is about six to seven inches long. Its most usual colors are green, brown, yellow, or gray. It changes from one color to another in one, two, or at most three minutes.

The swift. The *common lizard* or swift, another highly variable species, is found as far north as Michigan. It is of a greenish, bluish, or bronze color, with black wavy crossbands above. It is found in woods and along fences. The old rail fences were once a favorite resort of this and other lizards. Some of the charm of the Great Outdoors, of forest, field, and stream, has gone or is going rapidly with the old rail fence.

There are twenty-six varieties of swifts found in the United States alone.

Photograph by M. Graham Netting
FIG. 47. *A horned lizard, showing the spines. See page 54*

FIG. 48. *A horned lizard, showing how its color and pattern blend with its surroundings*

FIG. 49.   *Old World chameleons*

The horned lizards. The most interesting lizards perhaps are the so-called "horned toads," which should properly be called horned lizards. They are tailed, whereas no frog or toad has a tail. It is true that their body is broad like that of a toad and is also rough, warty, and of various brown and gray colors. But the horned toads are lizards, as their skeleton and internal anatomy show. They get their name from the fact that there are several or many spines on the head and neck. This makes them appear rather formidable, but as a matter of fact they are very gentle.

Courtesy N. Y. Zoölogical Society

FIG. 50. *The glass snake*

One may handle them with impunity; they rather seem to like it. Horned lizards live in the Southwest, although one species, the *ornate horned lizard* (shown on page 52), is found as far north as Canada in its western range. The horned lizard is viviparous, bringing forth living young up to ten in number. When handled these lizards sometimes feign death or injury, or send out *thin jets of blood* from their eyes, a most peculiar maneuver of defense. Their food is insects.

Several horned lizards that I kept for a while in a sand box would with great rapidity dig themselves into the sand when some one approached the box. Then, because of their gray and brown coloring, they were all but invisible. A number escaped from the box, and for two summers thereafter they could be seen darting about in the garden. They had come through the winter successfully in the latitude of Chicago, which is not excessively balmy.

Fig. 51. *The rhinoceros iguana*

The glass snake. The glass snake or *joint snake*, although snakelike in appearance, also belongs to the lizard family, because it has present in its skeleton both shoulder girdle and pelvic girdle. It has also rudimentary legs, which may or may not be noticeable outside. It gets its second name from the ease with which it can lose its tail, leaving it, perhaps in several pieces, in the hand of the one trying to catch it. To say that a glass snake is able to break itself into a number of pieces and then unite them again is, of course, a foolish and erroneous statement.

The iguanas. From Arizona southward and in the tropics are found the iguanas, large lizards with peculiar plates and frills on the head and along the backbone, and a huge dewlap on the throat. Although they look dangerous, they are entirely harmless. Their flesh is even good to eat. Because of its appearance, the iguana reminds one of the fantastic pictures of imaginary monsters, such as the dragons.

FIG. 52.   *The gila monster*

The Gila monster. The only lizard that may be called dangerous, among those in the United States at least, is the Gila (hē'lȧ) monster found in Arizona. This lizard reaches a length of twenty inches. Its color, black and orange, or salmon pink, seems to be a warning coloration, a danger signal among animals. This warning is quite in order, for the Gila monster is poisonous. Sometimes its bite does not seem to have any bad results, but there are times when it proves fatal. A number of years ago a state school superintendent who was bitten by a Gila monster died from the effects of the bite. The toxic qualities of this lizard's poisonous secretion seem to depend largely on its physical condition and as to whether it is angry or not. It is possible that the state of the weather may have something to do with it—no one seems to know. No wonder the Gila monster can afford to be slow, easy-going, and quite unlike other lizards. Here we have a creature that is poisonous, at least at times, without having a poison gland. Its poison is simply its saliva, which seems to undergo chemical changes according to its temper, physical condition, or the weather.

The varanus. Quite recently a veritable giant among lizards has been discovered on Komodo Island, one of the smaller of the Sunda Islands in the Dutch East Indies.

Courtesy N. Y. Zoölogical Society

FIG. 53. *An Australian monitor*

After hearing vague reports about a terrible man-eating monster in the interior of the island, a party of white men succeeded in capturing an enormous lizard. This giant creature measured thirteen feet, but it is said sometimes to reach a length of twenty feet or more. This lizard lives in caves in the hills of the island, sallying forth to hunt mammals, birds, and other lizards. No wonder it spreads terror among the natives. The giant lizard of Komodo belongs to a group of large lizards called *monitors*. They usually attain a length of seven or eight feet and are found from Australia, through the islands of the Malay Archipelago and the Philippines, to Japan. Perhaps a creature something like this, or a crocodile, really was the basis for all the tales about dragons, such as those killed by St. George and other legendary heroes. There must have been some foundation of fact for these widely spread and widely believed tales.

In the tropics, too, is a group of lizards called *geckos*. They have suction pads on their toes, especially at the ends, enabling them to cling to any surface, even a ceiling, much as the flies do. They are as gentle and harmless as the horned lizards.

Courtesy N. Y. Zoölogical Society

FIG. 54. *A gecko, clinging to a glass pane in an aquarium*
Notice the suction pads on the toes.

THE TURTLES

Turtles, like snakes, cannot easily be mistaken for any other creatures. One need not look closely to discover whether the animal before him is a turtle or not. The bony shell into which the turtle can withdraw its head, legs, and tail is so characteristic of it that one is never in doubt about it. The upper shell is called the *carapace*; the lower, the *plastron*. These are connected on the side by bridges of bone. On the carapace are plates of horny material, which may just meet edge to edge, or may overlap. In some instances it is covered only with a thick, leathery, oily skin. The bony part of the carapace is formed by the growing together of the vertebrae, ribs, and a number of plates. As a rule the plastron is smaller than the carapace, and is not formed of the breastbone, but of nine separate pieces of bone. Thus the only movable parts of the skeleton are the head and neck, the legs, and the tail. To make up for the rigidity of the body the neck is extremely flexible, having eight vertebrae. The neck in some turtles, notably in the species called the *soft-shelled turtle*, is so long and slender as to suggest a snake. In the marine species the feet are broad flippers, resembling those of the seals; in the other species they are broad, webbed, and equipped with nails. The skull of the turtles is thicker than that of other reptiles, but the brain is very small. Indeed it does not seem to make much difference to the turtle whether it has a brain or not, for one lived six months after its brain had been removed.

Turtles have an astonishing tenacity of life. One in captivity at Paris lived six years without once eating.

Excepting force, only cold will kill a turtle. If its head is
cut off, for days afterward, if touched, the jaws will snap
and the legs will move. All the life processes of the turtles

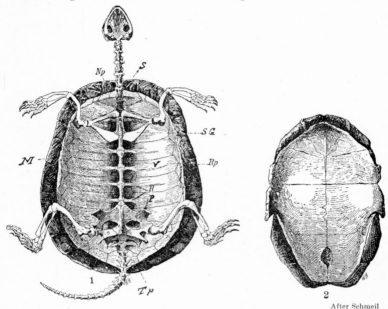

FIG. 55. *Skeleton and armor of turtle*

1, skeleton and carapace, and 2, plastron, both seen from the inside. *S*, spinal
column; *R*, ribs, fusing into the carapace; *SG*, shoulder girdle; *P*, pelvic girdle;
V, vertebral plates (the form assumed by the vertebrae; *Rp*, rib plates of carapace;
M, marginal plates of carapace; *Np*, neck plate; *Tp*, tail plate of carapace.

are sluggish, which explains why it is so difficult to kill them,
as well as the great age they sometimes attain. A turtle on
the island of Mauritius lived in captivity for over a hundred
years, and how old it was when captured is not known.

The mandibles of turtles are not furnished with teeth but,
like the bills of birds, are covered with horn, which makes
a sharp cutting edge.

Because their heart has only three chambers they have an incomplete double circulation. Their digestion is also simplified, as is their breathing. Since no distension of the thorax is possible, because of the bony box surrounding it, air is forced into the lungs by being swallowed. In addition to this they have in the pharyngeal region air chambers suggestive of gills. These keep up life when the turtles are hibernating in the mud at the bottoms of the streams and swamps, and pulmonary respiration is then

Photograph by M. Graham Netting

FIG. 56. *The snapping turtle*

suspended. Some turtles are herbivorous, others are carnivorous, while still others are omnivorous.

Turtles lay eggs, varying in number from a dozen up to a thousand. The eggs are laid in a hole made in the sand or ground by the female, and then covered up, the hatching being left to the heat of the sun. The mother does not in the least concern herself about her young, which are able to shift for themselves immediately after hatching. When the tiny turtles emerge from the sand, they at once make a bee line for the water. How do these tiny creatures know they should go to water, and how do they know in what direction it lies?

Although turtles are protected by their hard shell, yet they are preyed upon by certain large fishes, by alligators, and by the large cats, such as the puma and the leopard. The young, because of their softer shell, are even more at the mercy of these enemies. Their eggs are located and

5

FIG. 57. *The alligator snapping turtle*

stolen by such animals as the raccoon, mink, and skunk, and also by man.

Turtles are usually black, yellow, and red in color.

OUR COMMON TURTLES

The snapping turtle. The snapping turtle is about the only one that man need fear—that is, he must be careful not to give it a chance to snap at him with its vicious jaws, which can inflict a painful wound. Snapping turtles are always ready to bite for, like the water snake, they are bad tempered.

The carapace of the snapper, which is serrated at the rear end, has three blunt, broken keels running the long way. The plastron is very small, for otherwise there would not be room enough for the thick legs, neck, and tail. The tail is rather long, thick at the base, and covered with strong pointed plates. The head ends in a pair of keen-edged cutting mandibles, with which it is easy for the snapping turtle to amputate a finger or even the hand of a person.

Courtesy American Museum of Natural History
FIG. 58.   *The painted turtle with eggs*

The snapping turtle is carnivorous and voracious.   Among other things it will pull down swimming ducks and other waterfowl.   It can eat only *under* water, and it can remain there and in the mud for a long time without having to come up for air.   It reaches a length of up to three feet and a weight up to forty pounds.   A specimen in the collection at River Forest, Illinois, has a carapace fifteen and a half inches long, a tail eight inches long, and a head and neck six inches long, making a total length of twenty-nine and a half inches.   The *alligator snapping turtle* found in large streams in the South even reaches a length of forty inches and is correspondingly more dangerous.   Ditmars relates that one in captivity, when angered, bit off a piece of a broom handle without difficulty.

The painted turtle.   The painted turtle, one of the most common turtles, has a smooth carapace with no keel or serration on it.   It gets its name from the fact that there is much red coloration on the edge of the carapace and much yellow on the head and neck.   The plastron is a bright yellow.   The painted turtle lives in ponds and swamps,

Photograph by Raymond L. Ditmars; courtesy Am. Mus. Nat. Hist.
FIG. 59.   *The Cumberland terrapin*

Photograph by Raymond L. Ditmars; courtesy Am. Mus. Nat. Hist.
FIG. 60.   *The spotted turtle*

where it feeds on insects, tadpoles, plants, and fishes. A specimen in the collection at River Forest, Illinois, is eight and a half inches long.   It is, therefore, a small species.

The Cumberland terrapin.   Larger than the western painted turtle is the Cumberland terrapin, found from central Illinois to the Rio Grande.   It has a large crimson mark and yellow lines on each side of the head.

The map turtle.   Similar in size to the Cumberland terrapin is the map turtle, so called from the irregular yellow lines and marks on the olive carapace.   These marks resemble the lines on a map which indicate rivers.   The plastron is pure yellow. This species is found from Louisiana throughout the Mississippi valley and eastward to New York. It attains a length of twelve inches.

The spotted turtle. A pretty little turtle is the spotted turtle, found in ditches in the sand dunes of northwestern Indiana and from there east to the Atlantic. It is about six inches long, with bright yellow dots on its smooth carapace.

Photograph by Raymond L. Ditmars
Courtesy Am. Mus. Nat. Hist.

FIG. 61. *The three-toed box turtle*

The box turtle. The most interesting turtle in many respects is the box turtle, or rather the *box tortoise*. It has an arched, globular carapace, finely marked and engraved. The colors are black and yellow, but no two specimens are quite alike in their marking. On the posterior half the plastron has a hinge which allows the animal to close itself up after its head and legs have been drawn in, so that nothing can harm it. While other turtles also draw in head and legs under the carapace, the open space between the two halves of the armor is wide enough for the paws of small animals to reach in and tear out their vitals. Not so with the box tortoise. It is safe in its box, because the muscles holding the hinged part together are so strong that no animal can open it, for the simple reason that it can get no hold on the smooth box.

The box tortoise lives mainly on plant food, being especially fond of mushrooms. It seems to be immune to the poison contained in certain mushrooms. During a coal miners' strike in Pennsylvania many of the men roamed

FIG. 62.   *A soft-shelled turtle*

through the woods gathering berries.   Stumbling upon some
of these box tortoises, they took them home and cooked
them.   All who ate of the flesh were taken violently ill,
presumably from the poisonous mushrooms eaten by the
tortoises.

A box tortoise that I kept in my back yard remained out
of sight nearly all the time, but during a rain it would come
out of its hiding place and pompously stalk back and forth.
In the autumn it disappeared, having no doubt dug itself
into the soft ground a foot or two to hibernate, as the
tortoises usually do.

THE SOFT-SHELLED TURTLES

The large, flat turtles with a soft shell, often seen sunning
themselves on logs in rivers chiefly in the region south of
Chicago, go by the name of "soft-shelled turtles."   There
are four species of them in the United States, the better
known of which are the *southern* and the *spiny soft-shelled
turtles*.   A specimen of the spiny soft-shelled turtle in the

museum at River Forest, Illinois, measures twenty inches, of which twelve and a half inches is carapace. The neck is long and snakelike, this impression being heightened by the small size of the head, the diameter of which is the same as that of the neck. The tail is short and thick, tapering abruptly to a point. The large, flat carapace is soft and leathery. It is olive brown in color, with many small, black rings scattered over it. The large webs of the feet indicate that this species is even more aquatic than the others. As in the case of the snapping turtle, large specimens are dangerous to handle, for they can dart their head about with lightninglike rapidity and inflict ugly wounds. The soft-shelled turtles eat fishes, frogs, mollusks, and even fowl.

Courtesy Am. Mus. Nat. Hist.

FIG. 63. *The leather-back turtle*

Photograph by Raymond L. Ditmars
Courtesy Am. Mus. Nat. Hist.

FIG. 64. *The loggerhead turtle*

THE MARINE TURTLES

The leather-back or trunk turtle. The largest of all the turtles are those living in the ocean and on some of the oceanic islands. The leather-back or trunk turtle, for example, grows to be from six to seven feet long and may weigh as much as a thousand pounds. One in the American Museum of Natural History in New York measures nine feet across from tip to tip of flippers, as the paddle-shaped feet of these giants are called.

The loggerhead turtle. Another marine turtle is the loggerhead turtle, so called from the large size of its head. A skull of one from the Isle of Pines, Cuba, now in the collection at River Forest, Illinois, measures nine and a half inches by six and a half inches. The flesh of these sea monsters is dark and palatable, tasting much like beef. It is not often eaten, however, for these tortoises are seldom captured.

The green turtle. The green turtle, another giant sea turtle, attains a weight of from five to six hundred pounds. The average weight of those caught, however, is fifty pounds. This species is eagerly sought for by fishermen and others, for its flesh is much in demand. It is used for steaks and for the turtle soup so famous in our eastern coast cities.

The hawksbill turtle. A sea turtle that is even more important commercially than the green turtle is the hawksbill turtle, so called from the shape of its head, which is tapering and curved downward much like the bill of a hawk. While its flesh is eaten to some extent, its value lies chiefly in the large, horny shields or plates on the carapace. These are removed, polished, and under the name tortoise (tôr′tĭs) shell are made into combs and ornamental trinkets.

The giant or elephant tortoise. The giant or elephant tortoise is in some respects the most famous of the big turtles. Formerly it was found on a number of tropical islands, but now it is making its last stand on the Galápagos Islands, about five hundred miles west from Ecuador, South America. While not quite so huge as the leatherback or trunk turtle, it is large and ponderous enough. One kept in captivity on the island of Mauritius, in the Indian Ocean,

From *The Turtles of New England*, by Harold L. Babcock

FIG. 65.   *The green turtle*

From *The Turtles of New England*, by Harold L. Babcock

FIG. 66.   *The hawksbill turtle*

Notice the flipper-like legs.

Photograph by Elwin R. Sanborn; courtesy N. Y. Zoölogical Society

FIG. 67.   *The giant or elephant tortoise*

east of Africa near Madagascar, was able to walk away with
two men on its back, while one in the possession of Lord
Rothschild in England easily carries one man.   The turtle
on Mauritius measured eight feet six inches in circum-
ference, and its carapace was four feet long in a straight
line—that is, not counting the curvature.   It lived to the
ripe old age of about two hundred years.

Darwin states that he found thousands of these turtles
on the Galápagos Islands.   It required six men to lift one
of the largest males, which yielded two hundred pounds of
good nutritious meat.   This explains the rapid disappear-
ance of the species.   After sailors found the meat of these
turtles to be very palatable, they would descend upon the
islands where they were found and sometimes capture

hundreds of them and load them in the hold of their vessels, to be slaughtered and used for food during the voyage. The capture was made easy because these tortoises are more terrestrial than aquatic, and extremely slow and cumbersome in their movements, so they could not escape by running away. Since they are slow land animals, their food is entirely plant life, which explains the fine flavor of the meat.

The eggs of these large sea turtles and of the elephant tortoise are much sought after by people living on or near

Photograph by Raymond L. Ditmars; courtesy Am. Mus. Nat. Hist.
FIG. 68.   *Musk turtles, showing plastron as well as carapace*

these lonely islands. The huge marine turtles spend nearly all their time out in the ocean looking for animal or plant food. But when their egg-laying time comes they have to come ashore. Here they look for sandy places, where they scoop out great holes in which they deposit, in repeated layings, up to a thousand eggs. These are greedily sought by the natives and used as food. A large part of the food of the Indians living along the Amazon River, South America, consists of the eggs of the numerous large turtles found in this giant river.

The flesh of some of the fresh-water turtles is also used for food, the best known of these turtles being the *diamond-back terrapin.* It is not entirely a fresh-water species, since it lives in the salt marshes along our Atlantic and Gulf

Photograph by W. Bryant Tyrrell

FIG. 69. *Blanding's turtle*

coast, from Massachusetts on south. The finely flavored flesh of this species is in such demand that in New York thirty to forty dollars is paid for a dozen six-inch specimens. Every additional inch makes the price mount higher. For this reason this pretty little terrapin has been exterminated over much of its range.

Other fresh-water turtles whose flesh is used for food, or at least for a delicacy, are the *snapping, Blanding's,* the *map,* and the *spiny soft-shelled turtles.* Whoever has eaten soup made of a snapping turtle can testify to its fine flavor.

THE CROCODILIANS

In the order of crocodilians there is but one family, with several genera, of which two are represented in the United States.

In structure these animals resemble huge lizards, but they live in water more than on land. Their back is covered with rows of bony plates, each surmounted by a high, sharp ridge. The legs, tail, and abdomen are covered with coarse, tough, leathery shields. The crocodilians differ from all the other reptiles in having a four-chambered heart, and thus a complete double circulation of the blood. They have

Courtesy Field Museum

FIG. 70.   *Skull of alligator*

Courtesy Field Museum

FIG. 71.   *Skull of crocodile*

a valvelike arrangement at the upper end of the gullet which enables them to open the mouth under water and seize their prey without getting their lungs and stomach full of water. The tail is thick and muscular, becoming laterally compressed near the end. It serves the crocodile as a rudder while swimming under water and also as a powerful weapon, with which it can knock an enemy off his feet and sweep him toward its powerful, tooth-studded jaws.

The alligator. The alligator is found in our southern states from North Carolina to Florida, and from there to the Rio Grande in Texas. It reaches a length of sixteen feet, but owing to man's persistent, relentless persecution,

FIG. 72.   *An alligator pool*

Photograph by Julian A. Dimoch; courtesy Am. Mus. Nat. Hist.

FIG. 73. *An alligator crawling into the water*

Photograph by Raymond L. Ditmars; courtesy Am. Mus. Nat. Hist.

FIG. 74. *The broad-nosed crocodile*

such large ones are now rare. In muddy, murky ponds, surrounded by large old trees festooned with "Spanish moss," seldom visited by people because here also lurk the water moccasin and the diamond-back rattlesnake, now and then an alligator from ten to twelve feet long may still be found.

The old bull alligators give a loud, tremulous roar or bellow, at the same time emitting a strong musky odor which a breeze may carry for a mile or more.

The alligator, being extremely timid, will usually give man a wide berth, but when retreat to the water is cut off it will occasionally put up a stiff fight.

After Brehm

FIG. 75. *The gavial*

Alligators eat mammals, birds, and fish. A favorite titbit of theirs seems to be dogs, which they grasp, draw under water to be drowned, and then hold above water and swallow with one gulp. Unlike turtles and crocodiles, alligators cannot swallow food below water.

The crocodile. It was not known until 1875 that the crocodile also lives within the boundaries of the United States. In that year Hornaday found it in southern

Florida. From there it ranges southward to South America. The chief difference between the crocodile and the alligator is that the former has a narrow head and snout, the latter a broad one. The crocodile walks with its body higher above ground than does the alligator, which almost drags its body on the ground.

The man-eating crocodiles are found chiefly in Africa and Asia. In India, for instance, the crocodile levies almost as high a toll on human life as does the tiger or the cobra. In that country is found the largest of all reptiles, the *gavial*, which attains a length of thirty feet, although the average length is from twenty to twenty-five feet. But it is simply a crocodile with an enormously long-drawn-out, narrow snout and tail.

AMPHIBIANS

From *The Frog Book*, by Mary C. Dickerson
Copyright 1906 by Doubleday, Doran and Company, Inc.

The leopard frog

The commonest frog over much of North America.

THE AMPHIBIANS

Amphibians are changeable-blooded vertebrates that have neither hair nor feathers nor scales. Their skin is naked. That is about all one can say in describing them, for in all other respects they are more or less like certain other vertebrates. The name "amphibian" is derived from two Greek words meaning "two" or "both," and "life." It is an appropriate name, for these creatures lead a double life, partly on land and partly in water. All amphibians begin life in the water, while they may or may not continue their life on land. Take for example the salamanders, which are amphibians. Superficially they resemble the lizards. Then why not class them with the reptiles? Because the salamanders, unlike the lizards, pass a larval stage in the water. During this time they breathe through gills, but later they live on land and breathe by means of lungs. In

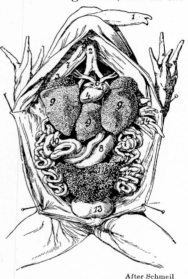

After Schmeil

FIG. 76. *Internal organs of amphibian (frog)*

1, tongue, thrust out of mouth; 2, windpipe; 3, lung; 4, ventricle of heart; 5, auricle of heart; 6, main artery; 7, gullet; 8, stomach; 9, liver, consisting of three lobes; 10, intestine; 11, ovary; 12, oviduct; 13, bladder; 14, lobed masses of fatty tissue.

breathing, however, the skin of the amphibians also comes into play, being used to a certain extent as an organ of breathing. Their skin, therefore, is naked, not covered with

FIG. 77. *Egg masses of frogs*

1, egg masses of wood frog; 2, egg masses of leopard frog; 3, egg mass of cricket frog (several such bunches are laid by one female); 4, egg masses of pickerel frog; 5, egg masses of green frog.

plates or scales as is that of reptiles and fishes. It is either smooth, as in the frogs and salamanders, or rough and warty, as in the toads. If this skin should ever dry out it means death to the animal; hence their insistence on living in wet or at least moist places.

There are two orders of amphibians, frogs and toads forming the one order and salamanders the other. Or the two orders of amphibians may be classified as tailless and tailed batrachians.

Most interesting in the life history of frogs and toads are the changes through which they go from egg to adult life. In the spring all frogs and toads, even those that spend most of their time in trees, are found first in the water of ponds and swamps. Here they have hibernated in the mud at the bottom.

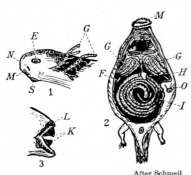

After Schmeil

FIG. 78. *Two tadpoles of frog (enlarged)*

1, head of young larva. *G*, outside gills; *E*, location of eye; *N*, location of nose; *M*, location of mouth; *S*, suction pore.

2, older larva or tadpole, with tail partly removed and body opened from below. *I*, intestine; *O*, outlet for water used in breathing through the inside gills; *H*, heart; *G*, gills (inside); *M*, mouth, showing the small horny teeth; *F*, rudimentary foreleg.

3, mouth of same larva, seen from side. *K*, horny jaws; *L*, lip.

These creatures are cold blooded, or rather changeable blooded; that is, the temperature of their blood changes with the temperature of their environment. When it becomes cold, their life processes are slowed up and become sluggish. Since their lungs are not of such a high order as those of birds and mammals, and since they have an incomplete double circulation of the blood, their life processes at best are not very active. In autumn when the air grows more chilly they become sleepy, sluggish, and finally torpid. During winter, animation is completely suspended. But when the spring sun first warms earth and water, they shake off their lethargy and come out of the ground and mud. Then all amphibians, whether they have hibernated in the mud below the water or elsewhere, repair to the waters of some pond or swamp.

FIG. 79. *Skeleton of frog*
M, the two much elongated metatarsal bones.

After Schmeil

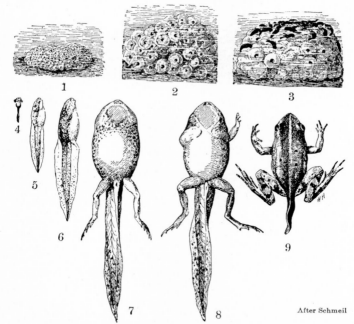

After Schmeil

FIG. 80. *Metamorphosis of frog*

All figures are natural size: 1, part of egg mass just spawned; 2, eggs several days later; 3, larvae or tadpoles just hatched, still on jelly-like eggshells; 4–8, older tadpoles; 9, young frog, with part of tadpole's tail still persisting.

Here they ovulate, or deposit their eggs. These are round, soft, and jelly-like. They may be deposited in the form of strings or in small round masses, or in large flat ones. Some are laid on the bottom in shallow water; others are fastened to pieces of wood or to plants. These eggs then absorb water and become larger and more gelatinous. In each egg can be seen a black dot. This is the embryo.

The embryo rapidly becomes larger, and in from three to four days, or in as many weeks, depending upon the temperature and on the species, the young are hatched. But

From *North American Anura*, by Albert Hazen Wright

FIG. 81.   *Mouth parts of mature tadpole of pickerel frog*
The mouth parts of other tadpoles are much like these shown here.

they are quite different from the adults. They are in a so-called larval stage in which they are known as *tadpoles* or *polliwogs*. They have no legs at all, but only a laterally compressed tail. Their mouth is equipped with several rows of tiny, rasplike teeth with which they scrape plant tissue from the leaves of water plants. For breathing they have bundles of external gills, but no lungs. They remain in this stage for two or three weeks or for months or, in the case of the bullfrog, for as many years. Then a peculiar metamorphosis, or change, takes place. In May or later you will notice hind legs appearing on the tadpole; then

Courtesy N. Y. Zoölogical Society

FIG. 82.   *Development of the frog*

the front legs push out, and finally the tail disappears, it being absorbed, not simply thrown off.   At the same time the mouth and gills of the tadpole are changing into the mouth and lungs of the frog.

The egg season of frogs lasts from March into June, our largest frog, the bullfrog, being the last one to come out of hibernation and to spawn, which in the latitude of Chicago is in the beginning of June.   The number of eggs varies from eight hundred in the case of the tiny spring peeper, to twenty thousand in the case of the giant bullfrog.   If all their eggs could come to maturity, the earth would soon be overrun with frogs.   But even while they are in the tadpole stage they have many enemies, which reduce their numbers woefully.   Fishes, herons, grebes, even the voracious larvae of certain insects, such as the dragon fly, diving beetle, and dobson, or hellgramite, all prey upon them.

The food of frogs is mostly insects, which they procure in a peculiar manner.   They will crawl up to a fly or moth and slap out their broad, sticky tongue at the prey and quickly draw it in.   This they can do because their tongue is fastened anteriorly, at the front edge of the mouth, not at the back.   So quickly does a frog catch a fly that our eye fails to see it.   One moment we see a fly; the next moment

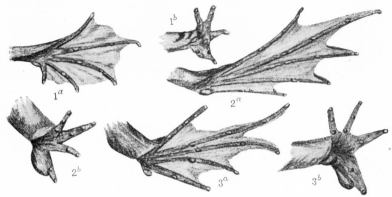

From *North American Anura*, by Albert Hazen Wright

FIG. 83.   *Hind feet* (a) *and forefeet* (b) *of breeding male frogs*
1, wood frog; 2, leopard frog; 3, pickerel frog.

it is gone.   The mouth of frogs is very large, almost cavernous, so that they can swallow large morsels.   A bullfrog has been seen to swallow a bluebird.

In the adult stage frogs still have many enemies with which to contend.   Swamp birds, snakes, hawks, even a number of mammals are not averse now and then to making a meal of a frog.   A frog's worst enemy, however, is man, who searches the margins of lake and river for frogs to use as food or as bait for fishing.   The frogs try to escape by swimming and diving, in which they are skillful because of their long hind legs that are webbed between the five toes.

On land frogs elude their enemies by the enormous jumps their long muscular hind legs enable them to make.   Then

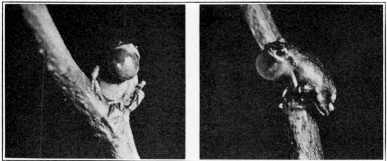

From *North American Anura*, by Albert Hazen Wright

FIG. 84. *Two views of the same croaking male peeper*
Note the mosquito on his leg.

there is their protective coloration. The colors are highly
variable in the same species, and even from time to time in
the same individual. In other words, like the chameleon,
they can change their colors. The frogs which live among
plants and leaves are mostly green, while those living on the
ground or on bark are gray and brown.

OUR MOST COMMON FROGS

(In the order of their appearance in the spring)

The spring peeper. When the warmth of the sun first
begins to be felt in March, but while the air is still raw and
chilly and the ice lingers in shaded pools, one will suddenly
hear a chorus of birdlike, cheerful peeps coming from a ditch
or a pool in the prairie or woodland. It is the voice of the
spring peeper or *Pickering's hyla*.

To most people it is only a voice, for they have never
seen its owner. And no wonder, for the hyla is very, very
small; in fact, it is the smallest of all our frogs, being only
about one inch in length, though the female may be a little
larger. Then, too, its color is brown and gray like the dead

vegetation among which it conceals itself. Often it will sit motionless under a dead leaf or piece of wood on the margin of the pool, or on a hummock in it. If you approach to

FIG. 85. *A spring peeper on a may-apple leaf*

learn the identity of these singers, they will suddenly hush and become motionless. No wonder that to many they remain only a voice! If you, however, also remain motionless for a while, you may suddenly see a little leaf in motion—a little bag, the throat pouch of a peeper, is being expanded. First one hyla will start peeping, then another, then a few more, until soon the concert is again in full swing.

If you stoop down to look at one of the tiny musicians, you will see that he is gray and brown and has a mark on his back like two y's joined inversely, thus:

From *North American Anura*, by
Albert Hazen Wright
FIG. 86. *An adult spring peeper*
Note the cross on his back.

In April the eggs of the peeper are laid. The adults then live on land in the vege-tation and bushes, and even in treetops, where they stay throughout the summer, hunting gnats, flies, and mosquitoes.

The tree frog. Better known than the spring peeper is the tree frog, wrongly called "tree toad." Once in a while,

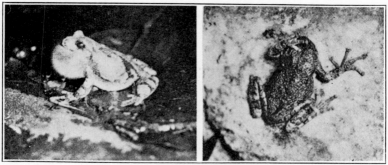

From *North American Anura*, by Albert Hazen Wright
FIG. 87. *A male tree frog*
Left, croaking; right, hit on head by hot flashlight powder.

when one places his hand on a fence post near a shaded farmhouse, he will withdraw it quickly with an unnecessary start of alarm. He was startled because he had placed his hand on a tree frog which unbeknown to him had taken up a position on the post. Why was it not seen? Because the color of the frog was gray just like that of the post. Or when walking in the wood or orchard, one will suddenly notice a little gray, brown, or green lump on a tree in the place where he just wanted to put his hand. Again the little bundle of life, a tree frog, was next to invisible.

Once, while visiting on a farm in Indiana, I was entertained every evening by a tree-frog concert. It was partly a birdlike warble, partly a croak, but withal pleasing to hear. The little musicians were all around on the roof of the house, on the windmill, on the pile of firewood, inside the milk house—in fact, anywhere and everywhere. When the tree frog sings or trills, the voice sac on the throat expands greatly.

The tree frog in color and in its ability to change its color is a good deal like the chameleon. It can and does change its color to blend with its surroundings.   The most common color is whitish gray, with brown markings on the back and legs.   In moist, dark places the tree frog's color

will often be dark brown; in green places it will be green. It cannot change its colors as rapidly as does the chameleon, often taking as long as an hour to make the change. The hyla may be distinguished from other tree frogs by the two whitish bands on the hind legs and the irregular starlike marking of dark color on the forward part of the back.

Courtesy Am. Mus. Nat. Hist.
FIG. 88.   *The wood frog*

The tree frog is two inches long and is found throughout eastern North America from Canada to Texas and west to Kansas.

The cricket frog.   Another tiny member of the hyla family found over most of the United States is the cricket frog, scarcely an inch in length.   In color it is usually some shade of brown, but this also may be changed.   It lives on the ground nearly all the time, so that it hardly seems to belong to the family of tree frogs.   It gets its name from its song, which somewhat resembles that of a cricket.

Other kinds of tree frogs are the *swamp cricket frog*, the *Florida tree frog*, the *green tree frog* of the southern states, and the *Pacific tree frog* of our northwestern coast and of Vancouver Island.

The wood frog.   The wood frog also puts in an appearance during the last week in March.   This is the brownest of

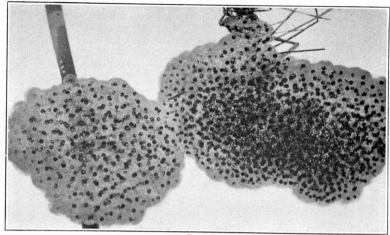

From *North American Anura*, by Albert Hazen Wright

Fig. 89. *Egg mass of the wood frog (left) compared with that of the leopard frog (right)*

our frogs, larger than the peeper but smaller than the leopard frog. The male is two inches long, the female, three. Its field mark is the patch of dark brown or black around the ear. Frogs have no external ear, but only a skin or tympanum stretched over the round opening to the inner ear. The range of the wood frog is northeastern North America, where, true to its name, it is most often found in damp woods.

The leopard frog. About the same time the wood frog comes out of his winter sleep, the gaudy leopard frog also appears upon the scene. It gets its name from the dark spots on its back and sides which resemble the markings of a leopard. The body color is mostly green, but this may change quickly to gray or brown. On the under side it is whitish. The folds of skin on the sides may be yellowish or bronze.

As in several species of the frogs, the eye of the leopard frog is golden. Altogether it is our finest looking frog. It is usually found in meadows not far away from water, where it will attract attention by its enormous leaps, making three or four in quick succession in an attempt to put as much space as possible between itself and anyone approaching it. In the spring the leopard frog joins in the choruses of peepers and toads. It is found over most of North America east of the Sierra Nevada. The southern leopard frog is even handsomer than the one in the North.

The leopard frog is called *spring frog* in Florida, *grass frog* in New York, *shad frog* in New England, and *meadow frog* in the Middle West. It is the most common frog in North America.

The pickerel frog. In appearance the pickerel frog is almost exactly like the leopard frog except that on the inside of the hind legs it is orange yellow instead of whitish. It comes out of hibernation about the first of April. Both the pickerel frog and the leopard frog are three inches in length, the females of each species being larger than the male.

THE TOADS

In normal seasons the first of April marks the appearance of the toad. This is a much misunderstood creature, which is not only harmless but very useful. Some one has figured out that each toad is worth $19.88 to a gardener or farmer. Its unlovely appearance, however, has led to its being looked upon with dislike, suspicion, and even fear. The toad certainly is anything but attractive, being rough, warty, and often black or mud-like in color. But with the toad, as with man, much of worth may often be hidden under a rough, uncouth appearance.

Photograph by A. M. Bailey

FIG. 90. *A striking example of protective pattern in coloration*
Here the toad's color and marking so blend with its surroundings as to make
it almost invisible.

In the autumn toads dig themselves into the ground, hibernating until April. Upon emerging from their winter quarters they immediately seek the nearest body of water and there deposit their long, wormlike strings of eggs. Here they may be seen and heard uttering their sweet, tremulous song. It is a distinct surprise to find such a sweet note coming from such a warty, rough-looking creature. Often a toad will keep on singing even after you have picked it up in your hand.

The skin of toads is not smooth like that of the frogs, but rough and warty. Behind the eyes are still larger swellings known as the parotoid glands. These secrete a white acrid fluid which the toads emit when in great pain or danger, as for instance when one is seized and bitten by a dog. The dog will immediately drop it and thereafter let toads alone. While the fluid is poisonous and may prove fatal to small animals, it is harmless to man. Toads have another fluid, a water-like, colorless one, which they will eject when handled. This is also entirely harmless and does not, as some people believe, cause warts.

7

Toads do most of their feeding at night. During the heat of the day they stay in moist, sheltered spots, for if their skin dries out it means death to them, because, as we

Courtesy Am. Mus. Nat. Hist.

FIG. 91. *The American toad*

have learned, their breathing is done partly through the skin. Often of an evening a toad can be seen hopping about around the back porch of a house looking for a meal. If not harmed, toads finally become tame and somewhat attached to a place and the people living there. If a pet toad is taken away some distance and then released, it will find its way back to the place from which it was taken, even though many miles away.

The usefulness of the toad consists in its ravenous appetite for insects. The way it devours May beetles, slugs, and caterpillars, even the hairy ones, would fill the farmer's or gardener's heart with joy if he only took time to watch. It catches flies by slapping out its broad, sticky tongue, which can be extended two inches.

Toads have much shorter hind legs than frogs and therefore cannot jump so well or so far. The skin is molted or shed from time to time and eaten.

Sometimes newspapers may report that at a certain place it has rained toads. The truth is that after a warm shower thousands of small toads are sometimes seen on walks, roads, and everywhere in the vicinity. These toads of course have not fallen from a cloud. It is the warm rain which has enticed them out of the water of the swamp or ditch where they were hatched. As it takes only a few days for toad eggs to hatch, and for the tadpoles to turn into adults, they are very small when able to leave the water—only a half inch or so in length. Their numbers are correspondingly large. The toad is found all over North America east of the Rockies. Other species of toads are found in the Rocky Mountain states, on the Pacific coast, and in the southern states.

Let us protect the toad, for it is useful and already has natural enemies enough. Snakes, owls, skunks, and other creatures attack it. The skunk rolls the toad over the ground to get rid of the poisonous fluid from the parotoid gland before eating it.

The Surinam toad. Surinam is another name for Dutch Guiana, South America. Here and in adjoining regions lives a toad with most remarkable habits. When the female has laid her eggs, the male packs or, to be modern, parks them on the back of the female. Here they stick, gradually sinking into the skin, which has become soft and spongy underneath them. Each egg rests in a little cuplike cavity, covered by a lidlike shell that is not a part of the skin. After a while young toads, not tadpoles, emerge from their prison. Thus the larval stage is omitted.

OTHER FROGS

The green frog. Several days after the toads come out of hibernation appears the green frog. True to its name, it is mostly green, with yellowish bands on the jaws and dark bars on the hind legs. It measures from three to five inches in length. The young green frogs often utter a kind of shriek or scream when one comes upon them unawares. Then with a high jump they will hurl themselves into the water, from which they are never far distant. The old frogs have a deep-toned, nasal, bass call—*chun-n-g* or *ktun-n-ng*. The green frog is found throughout eastern North America from Canada to Florida.

Courtesy Am. Mus. Nat. Hist.

FIG. 92. *The green frog*

The bullfrog. The largest of our frogs is the one to come out of hibernation last. This is the bullfrog, which does not appear until the end of May or even early in June. It grows to be seven or eight inches long. The largest one on record seems to be a frog received from Louisiana which measured nineteen inches with legs fully outstretched. The bullfrog has a large flat head with a huge, cavernous mouth and large elevated, gold-colored eyes. Behind the eyes is plainly noticeable the dark, smooth tympanum. The color is green or greenish brown, with or without spots above and below. The bullfrog is the most aquatic of all our frogs, never going away from the water, as do some of the other species. It eats crayfishes, snails, slugs, larvae of water insects, and similar delicacies.

The bullfrog does not sing in chorus as much as do the other frogs, but when it does the result is very startling. I have heard bullfrogs singing in something like a chorus, and in the distance it sounded like the roaring of a lion, or rather like the bellowing of wild bulls—hence the name "bullfrog."

Sometimes, when one is walking along a ditch or by a pond, lost in thought, he may suddenly be startled by a loud, deep bass voice, calling out *"more rum,"* or

Courtesy N. Y. Zoölogical Society

FIG. 93.   *The bullfrog*

"*jug-o-rum*," or "*go-round*." Thus the bullfrog greets one, and then instantly disappears in the water. The reason his voice is so resonant is because he has two internal vocal sacs in the pouch of the throat which open into the floor of the mouth.

The tadpoles of this species of frogs remain in that stage for two or even three years, reaching a length of six or seven inches. One often sees them in the shallow water near the shore of a pond or lake, some, perhaps, with the hind legs already grown, and others with all four legs, but with the tail still persisting.

The bullfrog is found all over eastern North America, west to the Rockies. Its remarkable bass voice has, however, been stilled on many a lake and pond where it was formerly a common sound. That is the work of the frog hunters, who kill as many of these bass soloists as they can for the sake of their hind legs, which are fine eating.

Let us do whatever we can so that not all these voices of pond, swamp, and lake shall be stilled.

The Rana areolata. Once when walking over a large prairie near Houston, Texas, we noticed a great many medium-sized frogs of rather pretty shape and pattern. They were light green, with numerous small round spots on the back, each spot bordered by a narrow yellow ring.

FIG. 94. *The crayfish-hole frog*

Upon approaching one, it would invariably disappear in a hole in the ground, usually that of a crayfish. This interesting frog goes under the name *Rana areolata*, for it really has no English name. As an appropriate name we would suggest *ground frog* or *crayfish-hole frog*. It is found only in the southern states, but even there it is not common and so is one of our rare frogs.

The Goliath frog. The largest frog in the world is the *Goliath frog* of the Cameroons and the Gabun region in western Africa. This frog, which grows to the size of a terrier, is hunted by the natives of that region, who prize its flesh highly. Frogs, lizards, and even snakes are, however, used for food in many other places also. I know of a Mexican family living on the ranch of a friend in Texas who made a meal of a large rattlesnake they had killed. Thus do tastes in food differ.

Camp's frog. In a tiny frog, called Camp's frog, found only near Brownsville, Texas, the larval stage is also omitted. (It gets its name from R. D. Camp, a naturalist and collector of Brownsville who collected much valuable natural-history material for the museums and universities of the country. He died suddenly on August 6, 1929.) When the young of this species leave the eggs they are frogs, not tadpoles. This is true, too, of many small frogs in the tropics, when there is no water at hand. Thus does nature vary her processes to fit the various needs of her creatures.

SALAMANDERS AND ALLIED SPECIES

Salamanders and other tailed amphibians resemble the lizards in many ways, but can be distinguished from them at once by their slowness of motion. The lizards are incredibly swift in their movements when in danger, while the salamanders are extremely slow. Moreover, the tail of some of these amphibians is vertically compressed, whereas in all lizards it is round. No matter how far away from water they may later round out their lives, they all begin in the water. Some of these forms, indeed, never seem to get out of the larval stage, as they keep the external gills throughout life. That means that such creatures —the newts, for example—live in water during their whole life.

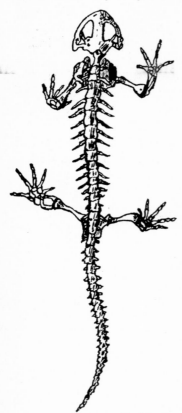

After Schmeil

FIG. 95. *Skeleton of a salamander*

SALAMANDERS

The spotted salamander. The spotted salamander is sometimes found in cellars, under outside steps, and in similar dark, moist places. In color it is black with whitish yellow spots. Since it is so slow in its movements that

Courtesy Mus. Nat. Hist., University of Michigan

FIG. 96.   *The spotted salamander*

it can never escape by running away, it has a special means of protection.   If handled, the pores over its body excrete a white fluid, which gives a bluish hue to the black skin of the creature.   This makes it distasteful to animals and disgusting to man, so it is usually let alone.   Furthermore, its dark and dank habitat serves as a protection.   In spite of its unlovely appearance, this creature is useful to man, for it destroys the disgusting sow bugs and pill bugs which live in the same kind of places as the salamander does, and which often get into our food.   The salamander also eats centipedes, millepedes, and insects that stray into its haunts. Salamanders are extremely tenacious of life, which accounts for the myth of the ancient Greeks about salamanders being able to live in fire.   This, however, gives no one a right to torture even so lowly and sluggish a creature.   We should get away from the notion that it is permissible to inflict pain and cruelty on ugly animals.   Even such ugly creatures as the salamanders, because of some nice adaptations in their habits and life processes, are of interest.

The axolotl. In Mexico is found the axolotl, a closely allied species of the salamander. It lives in pools that dry up in the rainless season. When this happens, this creature then ceases to breathe through its gills, which it uses in water, but instead breathes through lungs, and thus it is enabled to live in the air. When the rainy season comes again, and the pools fill up once more, the axolotl changes back to gills; that is, these organs become enlarged and

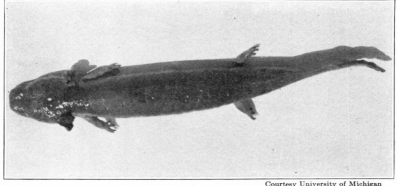

Courtesy University of Michigan

FIG. 97. *The mud puppy*

again function. That is carrying adaptation to environment to the limit. It is about the same as if we should use our legs for locomotion part of the time, then grow wings for flying through the air, only to lose them after a time and again use our legs. The axolotl is also able to reproduce, or lay eggs, while in the larval or tadpole stage, an almost unheard-of procedure. For all these tailed amphibians start life in the water and at first are tadpoles. Some naturalists consider the axolotl as nothing more than a larval salamander, which may under certain conditions develop into the salamander.

Other salamanders. One amphibian that apparently never gets farther than the tadpole stage is the *mud puppy, water dog,* or *necturus.* What boy, when fishing in a stream with a muddy bottom, has not at some time pulled out one of these creatures? They somewhat resemble a lizard, but have a flat head and body, a laterally or vertically compressed tail, and four small legs. In color they are uniformly dark brown. On each side of the neck may be seen a threefold red tuft. These tufts are the gills, which are retained throughout life. These mud puppies, therefore, are en-

Courtesy University of Michigan

FIG. 98. *Egg masses of the spotted salamander*

tirely aquatic. They are not poisonous, at least as to their bite, and when caught they should not be tortured to death. They are quite harmless, living on worms and other small water creatures. The mud puppies caught on hook and line usually measure from ten to fifteen inches in length, but they sometimes reach a length of two feet.

In ditches and pools in the southern states is found the *mud eel,* which like the mud puppy has outside gills but only two legs, the front ones. It grows to be a yard long, and a sudden view of it is somewhat startling, but the creature is entirely harmless.

The *hellbender,* or "alligator" of the Ohio River and its tributaries, is an ungainly and ugly looking but harmless creature. It has a brown, rough, warty body and four legs, but no external gills. In length it usually measures about two feet.

In woods, under moist decaying logs, is found the pretty little *red salamander* which, as its name indicates, is bright vermilion or brownish-red in color. It is marked with a number of darker dots. This harmless creature is so slow in motion that it cannot escape danger by flight.

After Schmeil

FIG. 99. *Newts*

The *newt* or *eft* is a pretty little creature found in ponds, ditches, and pools in the eastern states. Above, it is green or reddish of various shades, lemon yellow below with small black spots, and with scarlet spots on the sides, each bordered with a black ring. It is three and a half inches long, and makes an attractive aquarium specimen. A bright red variety with rougher skin lives away from water, under stones and bits of wood, coming out in the open after a rain.

FISHES

FIG. 100.   *Salmon jumping the falls at Oregon City, Oregon*

THE FISHES

The fishes are cold-blooded vertebrates adapted for life in the water.

How are fishes fitted for their life in the water? First, there is the spindle shape of the body, which we find also in water-cleaving mammals such as the otter and the seal, as well as in the mole which forces its way through the earth, and in the birds which cleave the air. Since fishes must cleave the water in order to get their food or to escape being made the food of others, their body is spindle-shaped and usually more or less laterally compressed.

Secondly, we note that instead of limbs, fish have fins. Their fins vary in shape, size, thickness, and rigidity. The diagram on page 112 shows the names given to the various fins. Some of them are strong and rigid and are called *rayfins*, because they consist of bony rays. Which fin makes possible the movement of fishes? The caudal or tail fin only, which alone is the propeller. The other fins merely aid the fish to maintain their upright position in the water and also serve as rudders, influencing the direction taken in swimming.

Thirdly, there are the gills. These are organs for breathing under water and for extracting the little oxygen in the water. The gills are located beneath the flap on each side of the head which is called the "gill cover" or *operculum*. If you cut one of these covers away, you will see four crescent-shaped, comblike masses of filaments. These are the gills. They are attached to slender, bony arches called "gill arches," which are hinged and movable. Water containing oxygen is taken in through the mouth and flows

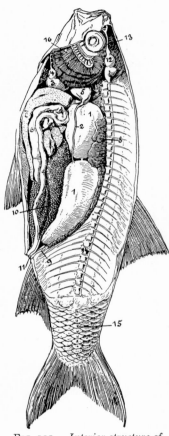

Fig. 101. *Interior structure of
a fish*

1, air bladder; 2, air duct; 3, heart;
4, artery, whose branches enter the
gills; 5, gullet; 6, intestine; 7, liver;
8, kidney; 9, ureter; 10, ovary; 11,
spawning duct; 12, brain; 13, olfac-
tory nerve; 14, backbone; 15, side
line; 16, gills.

over the gills, into which the blood is pumped. The carbon dioxide coming out through the very thin membranous covering of the gills is exchanged for the oxygen going in. This covering is dense enough to prevent water from getting in but thin enough to permit the oxygen to enter.

Fourthly, fishes have an air bladder. This is probably a gauge to warn them when they are out of the proper depth of water for which each species is evidently fitted. Some fishes, such as the top minnow, live at the surface of the water; others, such as the bass, live midway between the surface and bottom of streams and ponds; while still others, like the catfish, live only on the bottom. The air bladder also makes the fish buoyant. If the fish compresses this sac, it will sink lower; if it expands or inflates it, then it will rise. The bladder is connected with the alimentary canal, to be filled with air which is separated by the blood.

For protection, the body of a fish has a covering of scales, which overlap like shingles or touch at the edges; some fish, such as the sturgeon and gars, have strong bony plates and tubercles. The scales are the true inner skin, forming what is called an *exoskeleton*—that is, an outside skeleton. The slimy covering on the scales is the epiderm, or outer skin. Some fishes—as, for instance, the catfishes—are naked, having neither scales nor plates.

If one looks at the scale of a fish through a hand lens, he will notice that on it are circular lines or rings running

After Schmeil

FIG. 102. *Scales of fish*

These scales show lines of growth and the small canal found in the scales of the middle line on each side. These small canals run into a larger canal below, which is supposed to be the seat of a sense which we do not know—perhaps it tells the fish when they get into impure or too salty water.

parallel with the margin. Each year sees a line or ring added. They are, in other words, lines of growth, much like the lines on the shell of a clam or the rings that show across the cut of a tree trunk. Thus from a close examination of its scales one can determine the age of a fish.

Most of the fishes are predacious, each preying on smaller fishes. This is true from the largest to the smallest, which prey on the small fry just out of the eggs. For this reason, fishes have many teeth, not only in the jaws, but also frequently in the roof of the mouth and on the roof and floor of the pharynx. These teeth are not broad-topped and fitted

8

for chewing, but instead are needle-like, fit only to hold slippery prey. Quite a number of fish, however, are vegetarians, eating only plant food, from the tiny bacteria and diatoms to duckweed and larger plants. Some fishes are both plant and flesh eaters.

In front of the eyes of fish are the nostrils, which, however, do not enter the mouth, as in man, but lead into nasal sacs situated within the head above the roof of the mouth.

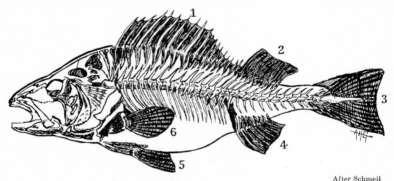

After Schmeil

FIG. 103. *Skeleton and fins of fish*
1, spiny dorsal fin; 2, soft dorsal fin; 3, caudal or tail fin; 4, anal fin;
5, ventral fin; 6, pectoral fin.

Fish also have ears, and it has been shown by experiment that they can hear.

The blood circulation in fishes is simpler than in the other vertebrates. Instead of three or four chambers in the heart, fishes have only two, an auricle and a ventricle; hence they have a simple blood circulation.

In the temperate zones in winter when the water becomes very cold, at least in the shallow water bodies, most fishes drop to the bottom, eat nothing, and become sluggish or half torpid. Even fish in an aquarium will do this, although the temperature in the room may be high.

Fish reproduce by laying eggs which are called *spawn*. The act of depositing spawn is called spawning. The eggs are produced in prodigious number, ranging from several hundred with the smaller fishes up to ten million and more in the case of the eel. This is a wise provision of nature. If all this spawn should hatch, and all the young live, the ocean would in a few years be a solid mass of fish. But as many more eggs are produced than is necessary for the survival of the various species, it is evident that a large part of the spawn and of the young fish can and does serve as food for the others.

Fish are coming to play an increasingly important part in the welfare of the people. Fishing serves as a source of recreation for many people who have been shut indoors for months. Each year these people go out into the open to the shores of rivers and lakes, where they fish to their heart's content. In most instances they do this not so much to provide food for themselves—although this is a consideration not to be ignored—but so as to find exhilaration in the open, to fill their lungs with pure air, to gain new strength in the air and sunshine. In this way the lowly finny tribe make an important contribution toward the good health and well-being of man. We should, therefore, do all we can to keep the rivers and lakes clean and wholesome, by shutting out sewage and pollution, and to restore to their former cleanness streams that have become defiled.

THE FISHING INDUSTRY IN THE UNITED STATES

How important the fisheries of the country are can be seen from the following figures. There are a hundred and ninety thousand persons employed in the fishing industry. The property invested in vessels, buildings, nets, and other equipment amounts to $210,000,000. About three billion pounds of fish, valued at $109,000,000, are sold annually. The fish are sold in various forms—frozen, salted, smoked, dried, and canned. There were sixty-nine million pounds of frozen fish sold in 1925. Canned fish to the value of $20,000,000 were exported in 1926. Yet in that same year we imported $50,000,000 worth of fish.

Massachusetts, on the Atlantic coast, is the foremost fishing state, with Gloucester (glŏs'tẽr) and Boston as the chief fishing centers. Portland, Maine, is also an important fishing port. It is an interesting sight to see the large fishing fleets of these cities sail out to the fishing banks. Some of the schooners sail only a little distance from shore and there go to work. Others go as far as the Grand Bank of Newfoundland, to the Georges Bank, or to any one of twenty other fishing centers. After days of hard labor, excitement, and often danger, they return with their varied catch. Then the fishermen receive their wages or a certain part of the value of the catch.

Connecticut fishermen in 1926 caught nine and a half million pounds of fish. New York City is a great center for the handling, distributing, and consumption of fish. In 1926 three hundred and ninety-four million pounds of fish, including a hundred and six varieties and valued

FIG. 104. *The drying reels of Lake fishermen*

at $30,000,000, were marketed in that city. This amount is equal to nineteen thousand carloads. Washington, on the widening of the Potomac River near Chesapeake Bay, is a favorable location for a fishing center, and here seven million pounds of fish, including forty-two species, are sold annually.

Another great fishing region in the United States and Canada is the Great Lakes. In 1918, the peak year for these fisheries, one hundred and forty-nine and a half million pounds of fish were taken from these waters. In 1926 the yield had decreased to a hundred and two million pounds, a yield made up of eighteen kinds of fish, of which chubs and lake herring or cisco led with forty-four million pounds. Lake Erie leads in the quantity of fish secured, Lake Huron is second, Lake Michigan third, Lake Superior fourth, and Lake Ontario last.

The Illinois River also contains and supports a wealth of fish, this stream yielding more than nearly any other river of its size.   Dr. Stephen A. Forbes,[1] head of the Illinois Natural History Survey, recently submitted the following figures for this productive river: in 1908 the commercial fisheries of the Illinois yielded nearly twenty-four million pounds of fish; in 1922, ten and a half million pounds.

On the west coast California is the chief fishing state, leading in this as in many other things.   In 1924 this state produced three hundred and twenty-eight million pounds of fish, which included forty species, valued at $8,000,000.

Seattle, Washington, is a great fishing port, in 1926 receiving thirteen million pounds of fish, worth $2,000,000. We shall discuss under "Salmon" the enormous catch of salmon in Alaska and in the Pacific states.

The chief food value of fish lies in the quantity of protein contained in the flesh, while the liver, notably that of the cod, contains much of vitamin A and vitamin D.   These vitamins are mysterious elements which must be present in one's food, for without them the healthful development of the human body is seriously interfered with and certain diseases may result.   Thus vitamin A, found in the liver of fishes, makes for growth, while a lack of it causes eye trouble and results in puny, weak bodies.   The lack of vitamin D, which like vitamin A is also found in the liver of fishes, results in rickets and poor teeth.

As in many industries, there was formerly great waste in the fishing industry, but this is being gradually eliminated. For instance, in 1926 a hundred thousand tons of fish meal and great quantities of fish oil were produced, largely from the offal of fisheries.   Quantities of these two products, however, are made from fish, such as menhaden and alewives, caught mainly for this purpose.

[1] Dr. Forbes has died since this was written, on March 13. 1930.

THE SHARKS AND RAYS

SHARKS

The lowest order of fishes. Although the sharks are the largest of all fishes, reaching, in the case of the whale shark, a length of forty feet, they belong to the lowest order of all the fishes. This is because they have no bony skeleton, but instead one of cartilage. Even the largest members of the skeleton, such as the jaws, are not bone. In spite of that these same jaws are equipped with row after row of cruel, sharp teeth, more or less three-cornered in shape. These teeth may be turned back and down to the floor or roof of the mouth, or they may be erected. The gullet of the shark is enormous.

After Schmeil
FIG. 105. *The jaws of a shark*
Notice the several rows of triangular teeth.

This large number of teeth indicates that the sharks are extremely voracious and destructive. They are among fishes what the killer whale is among sea mammals, or the tiger among land animals. They are the terror of the sea. Some of them do not hesitate even to attack man.

In most sharks the mouth is located on the lower side of the head, some distance back from the tip of the snout. Many eyewitnesses assert that when sharks make an attack they turn over on the back, just as the sperm whale does. This statement, however, is strenuously denied by observers who claim to know the facts.

The tail of sharks is heterocercal, that is, one fluke is much larger than the other, the vertebrae of the spinal column extending into the larger upper half. Sharks have no

Courtesy Field Museum

FIG. 106.   *A mother shark with her young*
The young sharks are spotted

scales, only naked skin.   Neither have they an operculum
or gill cover.   They have instead from five to seven slits
on the sides of the head, out of which the water runs after
having laved the gills.   Most sharks reproduce by means
of eggs, some of which are square in form with a strong
chitinous covering and with filaments, probably intended
to fasten the eggs to some support.   Yet a few sharks
are viviparous.

The common sharks.   The smallest shark, the *dogfish*, is
three feet long and is found in numbers on the coast of
Florida, and in most seas.   An odd-looking shark is the
hammer-headed shark, which grows to be fifteen to twenty
feet long.   The *sand* and *mackerel sharks* are six to eight
feet long, whereas the *great white shark* reaches a length of
twenty-five feet, and the *basking shark* one of thirty-five
feet.   These last two are the most voracious of all sharks,
not hesitating to attack man.   The largest shark, and at the
same time the largest fish afloat, is the *whale shark*.   It is
really an inhabitant of the warm oceans and has most often
been seen near the Cape of Good Hope.   A few whale sharks
have run ashore on the coast of Florida, one of which,
measuring forty feet in length, was skinned and mounted

by a taxidermist and then taken around and placed on exhibition in the large cities of the country.

The food of sharks is any creature in the ocean that they can swallow. Occasionally they attack whales, tearing out large chunks from their bodies. They also attack seals, cod, and mackerel. Most of the sharks live in the warm parts of the oceans, only a few coming regularly as far north as Maine. Only one lives as far north as Greenland. Sharks are often seen following a small fish, called the pilot fish, which they never harm, for it seems to pilot them to food.

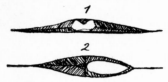

FIG. 107. *Cross sections of two fishes compared* 1, a ray, and 2, a flat fish, such as a halibut.

THE RAYS

The rays or skates. The rays or skates, the first cousins of the sharks, usually have a broad, flat body which in some is almost triangular, while in others it is more nearly round. Both eyes of the rays are on the upper surface of the head. The gill openings are on the under surface. The rays have a long, whiplike tail, with or without a spine or sting on it, with which they can inflict painful injuries.

The common skate or *tobacco-box skate*, of our eastern coast, is about one and a half feet long. Its young are often very plentiful in parts of New York Bay. The *torpedo* or *electric ray* can give one quite a severe shock. It attains a length of three to five feet and is found in the Atlantic Ocean south of Cape Cod and also in the Pacific and Indian oceans. The *sting ray* or *stingaree*, a hideous monster, reaches a length of twelve feet. With its sting near the tip of the tail it can inflict a painful and even a dangerous wound. Still

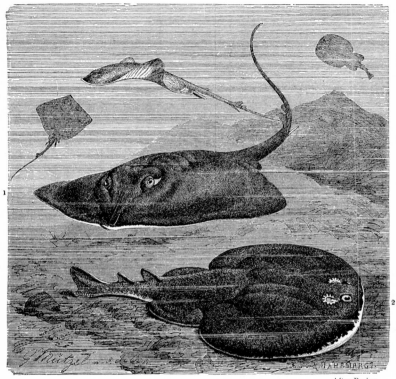

After Brehm

FIG. 108. *Electric rays*

it slips away if approached by a bather or by some one in a boat. In California it is called *beacher*.

The sawfish. The sawfish belongs to the ray family, although in form it is more like a shark. It is peculiar in having the upper jaw prolonged into the well-known form of the saw, which is studded with teeth on both sides. The sawfish has only two gill openings, which are behind the eyes.

The manta. The largest and most dreaded of all rays, and possibly of all fishes, is the manta or *sea devil.* This nightmare among sea creatures may be twelve feet long and twenty broad. The bodies of nearly all rays are flat and wider than they are long. Like a carpet or an ominous cloud, the evil-looking manta floats along and quickly settles down on its intended prey, enveloping it with its winglike body, and devouring it. Its mouth is huge and full of rows of teeth. The pearl divers of Panama and of the Pacific islands are not nearly so afraid of sharks as they are of this dreadful creature. They will readily attack a shark with the long knives which they carry for this purpose in their belt, but they become panic-stricken when they see a manta floating along above them. Although the South Sea islanders have little fear of anything found in the sea, not even of the dreaded octopus, if they see a manta floating on the surface of the sea they are stricken with fear and will not attack it even from a boat.

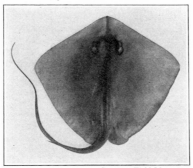

Courtesy Field Museum

FIG. 109. *The stingaree*

THE GANOID FISHES

The ganoid fishes belong to the lowest order of true fishes, the sharks not being considered true fishes. They have no scales, but instead shell-like tubercles or bony plates which touch on their edges. Some of them have a bony skeleton, while that of others is of gristle or cartilage.

THE PADDLEFISH

The paddlefish or spoonbill. To the family of ganoid fishes belongs the peculiar paddlefish or spoonbill, so called

FIG. 110. *The paddlefish*

from the broad, rounded, paddle-like projection of its upper jaw, measuring about one-third of the fish. It is found in the Mississippi River, and is common also in the lower Illinois River. Usually it reaches a length of from five to six feet. With its large head and its lower jaw set far back from the tip of the head, it has a decidedly sharklike appearance. It is one of our inland fishes, depending for its food on the smallest forms of animal and plant life in the rivers. For this reason there is on its gill arches an elaborate straining apparatus which keeps the fine mud out of its stomach. This fish is often taken by fishermen, much to their disgust, at Meredosia and Havana on the Illinois River, for it is not regarded as a desirable food fish. Its roe, or egg masses, however, is prized and made into a relish called caviar.

THE STURGEONS

The sturgeons. The sturgeons have five rows of keeled plates or shields on their body, one in the center of the back, one on each side of the back above, and one row on each side of the belly. As in the sharks, the tail is heterocercal; that is, the upper part is larger than the lower. On the lower side of the head, back a distance from the tip of the snout, is the mouth, surrounded by wormlike appendages. Sturgeons live both in the seas and in fresh-water lakes of northern regions. Those living in the Pacific and

FIG. 111. *Two sturgeons*
Upper, the white sturgeon; lower, the shovel-nosed sturgeon.

Atlantic oceans ascend the rivers to spawn. Such fishes are said to be *anadromous*, a Greek word which means "running upstream."

Sturgeons are bottom feeders, using their hard beak to stir up the mud for their food, which consists of worms, snails, insect larvae, small fishes, and water plants. They are sluggish fishes, and the larger and older they are, the more sluggish they become. They are content to lie like logs on the bottom of our large rivers and lakes. I have known instances in which fishermen on the Ottawa River in Canada thought their hook had been caught on a snag

on the bottom, whereas it was really inside one of these
large, lazy sturgeons, that was none too willing to be
brought to the surface.

The American sturgeons. The largest American sturgeons
are ten feet long, weighing about five hundred pounds.
The largest one ever caught, a *white* or *Oregon sturgeon*, was
thirteen feet long and weighed a thousand pounds. The
sturgeon of the Great Lakes and the Mississippi River
grows to be from five to nine feet long. So persistently has
it been caught for food, however, that it has now become
rare in most parts of its range. Still on the south shore of
Lake Michigan I have repeatedly found dead sturgeons that
had died of old age or disease. Before 1880 fishermen, when
they caught one of these big fellows in their nets, would kill
it and throw it into the water again. Gradually they awoke
to the fact that sturgeons are a valuable food fish, and began
to fish for them so diligently that their numbers soon became
greatly depleted. Thus, while in 1880 and during the next
few years nearly four million pounds of lake sturgeon were
caught by fishermen at Chicago, the annual catch had by
1900 dwindled to about a hundred thousand pounds. Pity
any creature of land or sea that can be turned into dollars
and cents!

The *shovel-nosed sturgeon*, shown on page 123, is fairly
common in the Mississippi, Ohio, and Missouri rivers.

The sturgeon in the Caspian Sea. The largest of all
sturgeons are those found in the Caspian Sea, lying between
southeastern Europe and Asia. Here have been caught
monsters that weighed three thousand pounds. It is not
surprising, therefore, to learn that Astrakhan, a city on the
northern shore of the Caspian Sea, leads in the manufacture
of the famous Russian caviar, a relish consisting of the

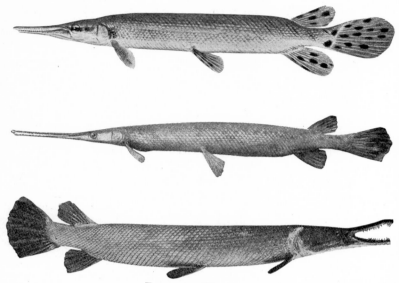

FIG. 112. *Three gars*
Upper, a short-nosed gar; middle, a long-nosed gar; lower, an alligator gar.

salt-cured eggs of the sturgeon.   When the roe of other fishes,
such as that of the paddlefish, is made into caviar, it is really
only an imitation of the genuine article made in Russia.
The egg masses are pressed out of the large spawning
sturgeons, and then the fishes are released for another crop
the next year.   That it is not difficult to obtain large
quantities of sturgeon roe is plain when we learn that one
female may carry from a million to two and a half million
eggs at one time.   This makes the sturgeon the most prolific
fish after the eel and perhaps the angler.

THE GAR PIKES

Varieties of gar pikes. The gar, gar pike, or *billfish*, both
long-nosed and short-nosed varieties, are long and slender

fishes, with a long bill-like mouth.   The mandibles of these
formidable jaws are lined with numerous strong teeth.   The
gars are covered with bony plates, which do not overlap,
but fit together like mosaic.   The *short-nosed* gar is about
three feet long, while the long-nosed species is five feet in
length.   The *alligator gar* of the Mississippi River and of
Reelfoot Lake in Tennessee grows to a length of ten feet
and longer.   All three varieties are extremely voracious

Fig. 113.   *A male dogfish*

and destructive to other fishes, and are therefore cordially
hated by fishermen.

Occasionally one may see a number of men with boats
and in hip boots seining our rivers in order to destroy as
many as possible of these pests.   These men are employed
by the State Fish Commission to do this work.   Often carp
and dogfish are also included in this work of destruction.
Voracious as these huge alligator gars are, their capacity
for killing fish must be truly enormous.   To the denizens
of the fresh waters they, no doubt, are what the sharks
are to those of the salt waters.

Like the eels, the gar pikes can remain out of water for
a long time without suffering serious consequences.   I once
caught a two-foot, long-nosed gar in the Fox River, forty
miles from Chicago, wrapped it in moist grass, packed it
in a suit case, and brought it to River Forest.   There I

released the fish in a classroom aquarium. Although it had been out of the water four hours, it immediately swam around as though nothing had happened. It did not even seem groggy from the experience because, in these fishes, the air bladder can be made to act as a lung.

The gars inhabit the lakes and larger rivers of eastern North America. The alligator gar is found in the rivers of the Mississippi system, from Illinois to the Gulf, and in Cuba and Mexico.

THE DOGFISH

An ugly ganoid. The *dogfish*, *bowfin*, or *mudfish* is another one of the ganoid fishes. It makes a somewhat unfavorable impression on the beholder. This fish has an evenly elongated, rather narrow body, embroidered by a long, narrow dorsal fin. In color it is dark olive, the male having a black spot bordered by an orange ring just in front of the tail. The dogfish, which is a greedy fish, lives on the bottom of muddy rivers and ponds, and even in

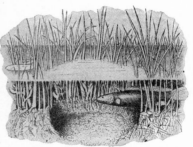

From *Parental Care among Fresh-Water Fishes*, by Theodore Gill

FIG. 114. *A bowfin approaching its nest*

swamps. Its appearance and movements strongly suggest the sharks. Once I saw a male surrounded by a swarm of young ones. The squirming mass of young rolled over toward the edge of the swampy pond where I stood. The eyes of the male, a few feet farther back from the edge of the pond, seemed to glow with rage as it moved and turned just like a shark. Like the gars, the dogfish is not

9

From *Parental Care among Fresh-Water Fishes*, by Theodore Gill

FIG. 115. *An African lungfish*

considered a food fish, although some people do eat it. The bowfin is found from Vermont to Dakota, and south to Florida and Texas.

THE LUNGFISHES

Fish with a real lung. The lungfishes are most remarkable creatures. Like the sharks and certain of the ganoid fishes, such as the sturgeons, catfish, and gars, they have a skeleton of gristle or cartilage. As in the gar pike, the air sac of the lungfishes can act as a lung, hence the name. In fact,

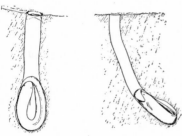

From *Parental Care among Fresh-Water Fishes*, by Theodore Gill

FIG. 116. *Diagrams of two dry-season burrows of the lungfish*

their air bladder is a real lung, although it consists of only one lobe, not of two as is the case in the higher vertebrates. But the lung of this fish gets blood from the heart to purify, somewhat as does our lung. There are several kinds of lungfishes, one or two being found in South America, as well as in Africa and in Australia. There these fishes live in swamps and pools where the water becomes stagnant and foul, lacking oxygen. Then sometimes, even when this is not the case, these fishes hold their heads out of the water, inhaling air into their lungs. They also have gills, but these do not seem to supply the fish with enough oxygen. When a river, pond, or swamp inhabited by the lungfishes dries up completely,

From *Parental Care among Fresh-Water Fishes*, by Theodore Gill

FIG. 117. *Another lungfish*

they bury themselves in the mud and animation is suspended. The mud around them is often baked hard by the intense heat, but when the rains come again this hard earth becomes soft. Then the lungfishes come back to life and swim around as though nothing had happened. They are clumsy looking creatures, sometimes six feet in length, and are very voracious. They can use their paired breast fins and ventral fins as if they were legs, so that they are able to move forward on land and even ascend slanting trees.

THE TRUE BONY FISHES

THE CATFISHES

The catfish. The true bony fishes make up by far the largest division of fishes, the lowest family among them being the catfishes. This is a very large family, numbering about a thousand species, thirty-four of which are found in the United States. Some of the species found in the ocean reach a huge size. Most catfish live in tropical waters, pre-

From *Parental Care among Fresh-Water Fishes*, by Theodore Gill

FIG. 118. *A catfish on its nest*

ferring sluggish streams with muddy bottoms. They are omnivorous, eating both plant and animal food and even carrion. Thus they act as scavengers and help to keep the waters clean and whole-some. They have a broad head with a barbel on each side, a capacious mouth, and no scales. Many catfish have the first ray of the pectoral fins developed into a stout spine, a weapon with which they can inflict painful stings, as many a boy has learned to his sorrow. Catfishes are very tenacious of life, their mouth opening and closing for a long time after the head is cut off. The spawning season of catfish comes in April and May.

Many people prefer catfish to other fish for food because they have only a few small bones, which can easily be removed. If caught in a clean river or lake their flesh is very good indeed. In 1926 a million pounds of catfish were taken in the Great Lakes alone by commercial fishermen.

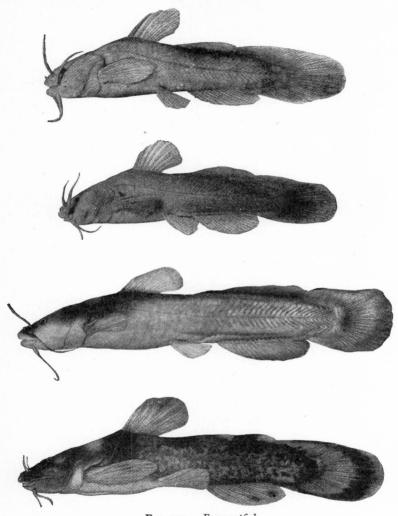

FIG. 119. *Four catfish*

First, a tadpole cat; second, a freckled stone cat; third, a slender stone cat; fourth, a brindled stone cat.

The best catfish for food is the *channel cat, silver cat,* or *white cat,* which reaches a length of three feet.   It is the best catfish for food because it lives in clearer and cleaner water than do the other varieties.   Being fond of mud-bottomed rivers, catfish with us attain their largest size in the Mississippi River and its tributaries.   Once, when walking along the shore of the Wabash in southern Illinois, I came upon two parties of fishermen in their boats.   Each party had a

FIG. 120.   *The channel cat*

large fish tethered to a stout stick on the bank.   On closer inspection the fish proved to be *mud cats,* or *goujons.*   They weighed thirty-five and fifty-eight pounds respectively. This species is not handsome—in fact, it is very unprepossessing in appearance—but it is good eating.

Varieties of catfish.   The *great* or *Mississippi cat* reaches a length of five feet and a weight of one hundred and fifty pounds.   Other well-known species are the *yellow cat,* the *red* or *willow cat,* the *Great Lakes cat,* the *Potomac cat,* the *stone cat,* and the *bullpout.*

The bullhead.   Of all catfishes the best known, especially to boys, is the bullhead or *horned pout,* which grows to be eighteen inches long.   This is the fish that never refuses to take a hook, no matter how poorly concealed by a worm, and then swallows it "all the way down."   With great pleasure I recall evenings of forty years ago on an old well-beloved farm on the St. Mary's River in Indiana, where I would hie after lessons were over on Friday afternoons and over holidays. On warm quiet evenings, after the day's labors on the farm were over, we would collect all the available fishpoles and, with a liberal supply of angleworms and a lantern or two, make our way down to the river, just below the large orchard. Soon the hooks were baited and thrown in. Immediately things became lively. The corks on the various lines would begin to bob up and down, and since each fisherman had several poles to tend, there was a great deal of running to and fro, while fish after fish was pulled out and tossed ashore. These fish were bullheads (*Ameiurus melas* and *Ameiurus nebulosus*). Every little while a cry of pain would be heard as a wily bullhead jerked its head aside and with its spine punctured the finger of an unfortunate fisherman. This mishap was usually greeted by a loud burst of laughter. The puncture, however, would have some disagreeable consequences, for the wound would become inflamed, and for a day or two be sore and painful. All this activity was punctuated by the telling of stories and jokes, the singing of songs, and the tending of a blazing fire. Suddenly, after we had caught perhaps thirty or forty bullheads, the bobbing of corks would cease. We had either exhausted the supply, or the swarm, disgusted by our treatment of them, had left for pastures new. The reason we went fishing at night was because catfish are more active at night than in the daytime.

The admirable work by Jordan and Evermann on *American Food and Game Fishes* contains an exceedingly humorous account of the bullhead from the pen of George Peck. The Milwaukee city council had resolved to withdraw the city water reservoir from the use of the fish commission for the hatching of whitefish. Peck thinks that this is as it should be, and advises the substitution of the bullhead for the whitefish. He says:

There are fish that should be propagated in the interest of the people. There is a fish that never looks at the clothes of the man who throws in the bait, a fish that takes whatever is thrown to it, and when once it has hold of the hook never tries to shake a friend, but submits to the inevitable, crosses its legs, and comes out on the bank and seems to enjoy being taken. It is a fish that is a friend of the poor, and one that will sacrifice itself in the interest of humanity. That is the fish that the state should adopt as its trademark, and cultivate friendly relations with, and stand by. We allude to the bullhead.

The bullhead never went back on a friend. To catch the bullhead it is not necessary to tempt his appetite with porterhouse steak, or to display an expensive lot of fishing tackle. A pin hook, a piece of liver, and a cistern pole are all the capital that is required to catch a bullhead. He lies upon the bottom of a pond or stream in the mud, thinking. There is no fish that does more thinking, or has a better head for grasping great questions, or chunks of liver, than the bullhead. His brain is large, his heart beats for humanity, and if he can't get liver, a piece of tin tomato can will make a meal for him. It is an interesting study to watch a boy catch a bullhead. The boy knows where the bullhead congregates, and when he throws in his hook it is dollars to buttons that "in the near future" he will get a bite.

The bullhead is democratic in all its instincts. If the boy's shirt is sleeveless, his hat crownless, and his pantaloons a bottomless pit, the bullhead will bite just as well as though the boy were dressed in purple and fine linen, with knee breeches and plaid stockings. The bullhead seems to be dozing on the muddy bottom, and a stranger would say that he would not bite. But wait! There is a movement of his continuation, and his cowcatcher moves gently toward the piece of liver. He does not wait to smell of it and canvass in his mind whether the liver is fresh. It makes no difference to him. He argues that here is a family out of meat. "My country calls and I must go," says the bullhead to himself, and he opens his mouth and the liver disappears.

It is not certain that the boy will think of his bait for half an hour, but the bullhead is in no hurry. He is in the mud and proceeds to digest the liver. He realizes that his days will not be long in the land, or water more properly speaking, and he argues that if he swallows the bait and digests it before the boy pulls him out, he will be just so much ahead. Finally, the boy thinks of his bait, pulls it out, and the bullhead is landed on the bank, and the boy cuts him open to get the hook out. Some fish only take the bait gingerly, and are only caught around the selvage of the mouth, and they are comparatively easy to dislodge. Not so with the bullhead. He says if liver is a good thing, you can't have too much of it, and it tastes good all the way down. The boy gets down on his knees to dissect the bullhead, and get his hook. . . . . There is one drawback to the bullhead, and that is his horns. We doubt if a boy ever descended into the patent insides of a bullhead to mine for limerick hooks, that did not, before his work was done, run a horn into his vital parts. But the boy seems to expect it, and the bullhead enjoys it. We have seen a bullhead lie on the bank and become dry, and to all appearances dead to all that was going on, and when a boy sat down on him and got a horn into his elbow and yelled murder, the bullhead would grin from ear to ear, and wag his tail as though applauding for an encore.

THE SUCKERS

The suckers. The suckers, which make up a large and well-known family, get their name from the fact that they live on the bottom of streams and suck up their food. This consists largely of vegetable matter, such as the roots and bulbs of water plants, and seeds, also worms, larvae, and the eggs of fish. The mouth of suckers is tubelike and bent downward. Their flesh is firm and well flavored, but hardly fit for food, owing to the presence of innumerable bundles of thin fagot bones.

In the spring suckers ascend streams to spawn. Then the small creeks flowing into a large lake are sometimes so filled with these fishes that they can literally be scooped out with a pitchfork or shovel. The best known members of

FIG. 121.   *Three suckers*
Upper, a spotted sucker; middle, a common sucker; lower, a hogsucker.

this family are the *chub sucker*, the *spotted* or *striped sucker*, the *long-nosed*, *northern*, or *red sucker*, the *common* or *fine-scaled sucker*, and the *hogsucker* or *stone roller*.

The buffalo fishes. To the sucker family belong the several species of buffalo fishes which inhabit the muddy streams and lakes of the Mississippi valley. Once, when I

Fig. 122. *The small-mouth buffalo fish*

was visiting in Missouri, the sons of my host said to me, "Let us go tickling fish."

"What do you mean by tickling fish?" I asked. "Do you mean that when they swallow the hook it probably tickles them on the inside?"

The boys laughed and said, "No; come along."

So we went to the near-by "branch," or muddy creek, which in summer, with the exception of a few deep holes, was often dry. The boys waded into one of these holes. When they approached a stump lying or standing in the water they cautiously felt their way with their hands between the roots. If they felt a buffalo fish there, they would work their hands up along the side of its body. Since the fish

was headed toward the solid stump, it could not get away.
When they reached the gill covers, the boys would instantly
sink their fingers into the mass of soft gills underneath them.

FIG. 123.   *The short-headed red horse*

FIG. 124.   *The stone roller*

This allowed them to get a good hold on the slippery
fish, and out it would come.   This is what they meant by
"tickling" fish!

Some buffalo fish are broad, humpbacked, and carplike;
others are narrower, more herring-like in shape, and also
silvery in color.   Some have large scales, while those of
others are small.   The *red horse*, which belongs in this
family, gets its name from the red color on its fins and the
adjoining parts of its body.

THE MINNOWS

The minnows comprise a large family, there being about two hundred and twenty-five species found in the waters of our country alone. Most minnows are small, reaching a length of only a few inches, though a few become larger. One must not call the young of any fish minnows. The proper designation of any young fish really is "fry." Minnows, which are found in swarms in even the smallest water courses, are active and swift in their movements. At breeding time the males of many species acquire bony tubercles and thornlike growths on the head, and also become more highly colored, notably red, as, for instance, the *red-bellied dace*. Certain minnows make the best possible live bait for angling for game fish.

The large minnows. The exception to the small size usual in the minnow family are such fish as the *squawfish* of the Columbia River, which reaches a length of four feet, and the *white salmon* of the Colorado River, which is incorrectly so called. This fish attains a length of five feet and sometimes weighs as much as eighty pounds. The German carp introduced into this country also belongs in this family.

The carp. The introduction of the carp into our waters was a great blunder, just as was the introduction into this country of the English sparrow. The carp was brought into the rivers of Illinois between the years 1879 and 1885. But carp are so prolific and make themselves at home so readily in new surroundings that by 1899 the catch of carp in the Illinois River alone amounted to over eight million pounds.

The carp wallows on the bottom of our streams, much as hogs wallow in the mud. In fact it may be called the hog among fishes. With their wallowing, the carp make clear streams muddy and uproot the bottom vegetation, thus destroying the plants that furnish food and shelter for such water birds as ducks.   Carp feed on leaves, roots, bulbs, and seeds of water plants, but they are also accused of eating the eggs or spawn of other fishes.   This would tend to lessen the number of other and better fishes, much as the English sparrow has ousted from our cities and villages the better native birds.   Dr. S. A. Forbes of the Illinois Natural

Fig. 125.   *European carp*
The commoner scaled form from rivers and muddier lakes.

History Survey, however, denies or at least seriously doubts the destructiveness of the carp.

As a food fish, the carp is not a great success, its flesh being coarse and not well flavored.   In some states the fish commissions employ men to seine carp out of the rivers and destroy them.   But this procedure will probably be as futile as is any attempt to exterminate the English sparrow.

The carp spawns in May and June, each female depositing from four hundred thousand to five hundred thousand small eggs.   This fish attains a length of two feet or more.   It has a stout, robust body, somewhat elevated on the back, thus resembling the buffalo fishes.   Its scales are the largest of any fresh-water fish.   There are two varieties of carp, one having the scales equally distributed over the body, the other having here and there short lines of unusually large scales. This fish is known as the *mirror carp*. In 1926, two and three-quarter million pounds of carp were taken in the Great Lakes alone by commercial fishermen.

The goldfish. The goldfish, which are natives of China, are close relatives of the carp and the minnows. Early in the eighteenth century they were introduced into Europe by way of Portugal and immediately found popular favor.

FIG. 126. *European carp*
This is a mirror carp.

Since they are easy to propagate, they were soon found everywhere. Of late the Japanese have in their fish culture produced many and startling varieties of goldfish, such as the elaborate *fantails*. With their bulging eyes and enormous tail and fins, some of these fishes are so artificial that to me they are almost repellent freaks. When they are kept in an aquarium, this should not be a small globular one where the fish are always nearly stifling for want of oxygen, but it should be large and open. For more information on this topic, read the article in the appendix, entitled "The Aquarium and Terrarium."

The small minnows. The little sprites that one sees darting about with incredible swiftness in the smallest

brooks meandering through the prairies or in a small
waterhole left after the drying up of a creek, are min-

nows. Many people think
these are simply young fish
that by and by will become
larger. That is not the case,
for minnows remain small
throughout life. Seen from
above, they all seem to be of
a dull, drab color, usually
black or brown. But when
viewed from the side, as seen
in an aquarium, they are very
attractive, not only in color
but also in shape. Their outline is extremely trim, like that
of a skiff built for speed. The
best known of the minnows
are the *stone rollers*, the *chubs*,
the *fallfish*, the *dace*, and the
shiners, notably the *golden
shiner*. The dace and the
shiners are fine species for the

FIG. 127.   *Four small minnows*
First, black-head minnow; second,
male bullhead minnow; third, female
bullhead minnow; fourth, Cayuga
minnow.

aquarium.   Other minnows are the *straw-colored*, the *fat-
head*, and the *blunt-nosed minnows*, and the *horned dace* or
creek chub.   The *eastern chub*, which spawns in May, builds
great heaps of pebbles in running water for a nest.   The
males do the building, carrying the pebbles in the mouth.
Once, for a long time, I kept a golden shiner in my aquarium.   This fish, the finest of the shiners, is ornamental
and easy to keep.   On the bottom of the aquarium lived a
stone roller, a *Johnny darter*, and a *mud minnow*, the last one

really not a minnow at all. The *red-bellied dace*, found in a number of the small prairie brooks around Chicago and to the south, is one of the finest of minnows for an aquarium. In the spring the male assumes a brilliant scarlet color on the belly and chin, while the fins become lemon yellow. The females are not so brightly colored.

FIG. 128. *The golden shiner*

The *bullhead minnow* exhibits delicate iridescent greenish and bluish shades on the sides. In the spring the *black-head minnow* has a golden glow with green and yellow. Nearly all minnows have on each side of the body a dark-colored line which seems to indicate the position of the backbone. Among other minnows are the *spot-tailed*, the *steel-colored*, the *sucker-mouthed*, the *redfin*, the *spotted shiner*, the *big-eyed*, and the *river chub*. The delicate, large-eyed top minnows really belong to the family of killifishes, while the mud minnows belong to the mudfishes.

THE HERRINGS AND ALLIED SPECIES

The tarpon. The tarpon is one of the most famous of all game fishes; in fact, Dr. Jordan[1] considers it the most famous. It is at the same time the largest game fish, with the exception of the tuna or tunny. The tarpon reaches a length of from two to six feet, and a weight of from thirty to more than three hundred pounds, but most of them weigh less than a hundred pounds. Specimens weighing more than two hundred pounds have been taken with hook and line, the largest with the harpoon. The tarpon is a handsome fish, silvery white in color and therefore called "silver

[1] David Starr Jordan, former president of Leland Stanford University, the greatest authority in the United States on fishes.

10

FIG. 129.   *The tarpon*

Compare the size of the tarpon with that of the menhaden, shown in the
lower left-hand corner.   Note the whiplike extension of the dorsal fin.

king."   Its scales are large, those of small specimens being
as big as a silver dollar, while those of larger ones measure
as much as three inches across.   Its eyes are also large.
The tarpon is found in the Gulf of Mexico, the principal
fishing grounds for it being the coast of Florida.   It is also a
common fish in the waters about Porto Rico.   Occasionally
one wanders even as far north as the Cape Cod region.   It
must be a thrilling experience to have one of these silvery
giants on the line and to watch it leap again and again out
of the briny waters in its attempt to shake the hook from
its mouth.

The common herring.   The herring undoubtedly is the
most important food fish in the world.   It is estimated that
about three billion herring weighing half as many pounds are
taken each year out of the North Sea and the Atlantic Ocean.
Herring are found in the temperate and colder parts of the
North Atlantic, and a very similar fish in the North Pacific.
The chief fishing centers for herring are the Grand Bank of
Newfoundland, a plateau which rises from the sea bottom
to within two hundred feet of the surface of the sea, and the
Dogger Banks, near the east coast of England in the North

HEINRICH HARDER

After Schmeil

Fig. 130. *Herring, pursued by codfish and haddocks*

Sea. Here at spawning time these fish gather in enormous schools—as fish moving together in great numbers are called. Herring are probably the greatest migrants among fishes. They migrate in masses of unbelievably large numbers, followed by their enemies, such as the cod, haddock,

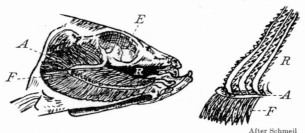

After Schmeil

FIG. 131. *Gills of a herring*

At the left, head of herring with one side cut away to show the outermost gill (somewhat less than natural size); to the right, part of a gill (slightly enlarged). *A*, gill arch; *F*, gill filaments; *R*, gill rakers, the enlarged drawing showing their minute teeth; *E*, eye socket.

porpoise, seal, and whale, which make great inroads in their numbers, but not so much as does man.

The food of herrings consists mostly of small creatures belonging to the crayfish tribe, such as small shrimps. Among other herring or near-herring are the *round*, the *tailor* or *fall herring*, the *glut* or *summer herring*, the *skipjack*, the *thread herring*, the *gizzard shad*—also called *hickory*, *mud*, and *white shad*—and the *alewife* or *branch herring*.

Large numbers of alewives are caught in the rivers and off the coast of our eastern states. They are found chiefly from North Carolina northward in about the same territory as the shad, but the alewife is not nearly so good a food fish. In 1926 no less than five and a half million pounds of alewives were caught in the Potomac River alone.

The "sardines." The so-called "sardines" packed in great quantities in Maine, Massachusetts, California, and elsewhere in this country are not real sardines, but the young of the common herring or of closely related species. Locally these fish are known as *cunners*. Real sardines are found only in the Mediterranean Sea. The packing of these young herring has become quite an important industry in this country. In Maine and Massachusetts alone there are thirty-five packing plants, their output in 1926 being nearly two million cases. In California there are thirty such plants, with an output of over two million cases. Here the California herring and the California sardine are packed under the name of sardines.

THE SHAD

Shad. The shad, a member of the herring family, lives in the ocean for three or four years, until it becomes mature. Then in the following spring it is seized by an irresistible impulse to spawn, for which purpose it ascends the rivers. Such fishes are said to be anadromous.

The early pioneers who settled in the eastern parts of our continent were astonished and delighted by the enormous numbers of shad running up the rivers in the spring to spawn. They soon found that these fish were delicious food, and saw to it that their catch was as large as possible. As a consequence of the continued taking of shad in great numbers, this fish became less and less abundant. Finally, the fish became so scarce that the federal government began to hatch them artificially and to restock the rivers. Now they are again abundant in our eastern rivers, so much so that in 1926 three hundred and thirty-six thousand shad, weighing a million pounds, were caught in the Potomac River alone. As a result, Maryland and Virginia rank high as fishing states, Maryland alone in this year employing over nineteen thousand men in commercial fishing. There are also shad fisheries on the Hudson and Connecticut rivers as well as in the rivers and along the coast of Virginia. The output of canned shad in Maryland, Virginia, and North Carolina was one hundred and fifteen thousand cases in 1926. Only the chinook salmon and the cod exceed the shad in value among all the fishes of the United States.

The United States Fish Commission has also introduced the shad into the Pacific as well as in such rivers emptying

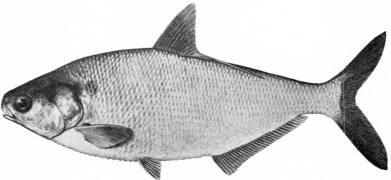

FIG. 132. *The gizzard shad*

into it as the Sacramento and the Columbia. The success has been so great that in 1926 the output of canned shad in Washington and Oregon alone was fifteen thousand cases. The shad is now common along the Pacific from San Diego to Fort Wrangel in Alaska. On the eastern coast it is found from Florida to Newfoundland, the center of abundance being from North Carolina to Long Island.

The shad, like the herring, is silvery in color, but has a more arched or slightly humped back. The shad bush— also called June berry, service berry, or sugar berry—gets its name from this fish, because it blooms early in the spring, just about the time the shad run up the rivers to spawn.

THE WORK OF THE UNITED STATES BUREAU OF FISHERIES

Honor to whom honor is due. Having just seen how valuable and important the work of the Bureau of Fisheries has been as regards the shad, we shall stop in our consideration of fishes just long enough to say something about this highly efficient organization.

The Bureau of Fisheries, formerly called the United States Fish Commission, is now a part of the Department of Commerce in Washington. It is composed of a commissioner who is at the head, a number of scientists and experts, and a large number of operatives and workers.

One branch of the activity of the bureau is the gathering of statistics or figures regarding the number, weight, and kinds of fish taken anywhere in the United States by commercial fishermen and fishing companies. This information is given in their reports and spread abroad. These reports are available to everybody.

The bureau also has experts at work in the technology of fishing—that is, they try to improve the methods and reduce the cost of fishing and thus lower the cost of fish to the consumer. They test out processes of preserving, freezing, canning, and packing fish in order to reduce the loss from spoiling and to get the fish to the consumer in as fresh and wholesome a condition as possible. They also investigate ways and means of improving fishing apparatus, such as nets and other gear.

Especially valuable is the work of the bureau in devising ways and means of preventing waste in the fishing industry and of utilizing the offal left in the preparation of fish for the market, especially at the canneries. As a result there has been developed an important industry in by-products,

FIG. 133.   *Hauling in the net*

such as making fish meal, fish oil, and fertilizer.   The importance of this industry may be seen from the following figures: in 1925 the production of fish and whale oil amounted to over thirteen million gallons, valued at $6,500,000; the fish meal produced was valued at $4,600,000 and the fish glue at $500,000.

Fish oil is used in many ways, some of which may seem surprising.   It is used for paint, and goes into the making of leather and printers' ink, linoleum, cork flooring, soap, and food fats.   It is also used for tempering steel, in mine lamps, and for lubrication.   Fish meal is used as a food for poultry and live stock and as a fertilizer.

Another activity of the bureau is making biological investigations, that is, life studies of the different kinds of fishes in order to find out their food, their enemies, their diseases, and the laws governing their increase and decrease from time to time.   These studies apply not only to fishes, but also to oysters, crabs, lobsters, clams, sponges, terrapin, fresh-water mussels, and even to the fur seals on the Pribilof Islands in Bering Sea, and to whales. Scientists are engaged in this work at the biological stations at Woods Hole, Massachusetts; Beaufort, North Carolina; Key West, Florida; and Fairport, Iowa.

Fish culture, however, is by far the most important part of the work of the bureau. This includes the propagation and distribution of food and game fishes, as we have seen is done in the case of the shad. During the season of 1927 the bureau collected eight billion fish eggs, including those of twenty-eight different kinds of fish, such as salmon, cod, mackerel, trout, whitefish, and shad. Then these eggs are hatched out artificially in fifty-five nurseries or hatcheries. From these hatcheries the Bureau of Fisheries in a single season placed in various rivers, lakes, and arms of the sea six and a half billion newly hatched fish, called fry, as well as somewhat larger ones, called fingerlings. To do this, the bureau worked together with commercial fishermen and companies at no less than eighty-nine stations. Except for this work of the bureau these eggs would in most instances have been a total loss so far as the future supply of fish is concerned.

The hatcheries maintained by the bureau are located in thirty-two states. Some are carried on in coöperation with state governments, with sportsmen's associations, and even with private individuals. To carry on this distribution of fish the bureau operates five railway cars, built especially for this purpose, which travel about seventy-five thousand miles in a year.

Another interesting work carried on by the Bureau of Fisheries is the saving of fish which have become landlocked

or marooned during a flood.   For instance, during the flood
of the Mississippi River in 1927 millions of fish were carried
with the flood waters over the inundated land, and when
the flood subsided they were left behind in the many pools,
which soon dried out.   During and after this flood the men

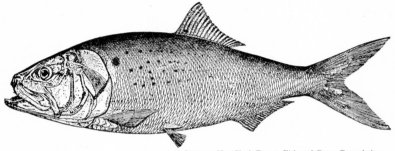

Courtesy New York Forest, Fish and Game Commission

FIG. 134.   *The menhaden*

of the bureau saved a hundred million fish and distributed
them to various rivers and lakes.

Thus we see that without the work of the Bureau of
Fisheries many a river, lake, or arm of the ocean would no
longer be able to supply members of the finny tribe for food,
or for recreation, as they now do.

In Canada much the same work is being done in the same
thorough and efficient manner by the Department of
Marine and Fisheries.   There is less need there, however, for
restocking rivers and lakes with fish, because the Cana-
dians do not allow their rivers to be used as sewers as is too
often done in the United States.

THE MENHADEN

The menhaden.   The menhaden is remarkable for two
reasons.   First, it is probably the most abundant fish on our
eastern coast.   Secondly, although a relative of the delicious

shad and caught in vast numbers, it is used but little for food. Instead, the menhaden is converted into fish oil and fish meal, and alone has given rise to an industry of considerable extent. It is also used as bait in various other fisheries.

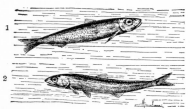

FIG. 135. *A sardine (1) and an anchovy (2)*

The menhaden is a small fish, twelve to eighteen inches in length. It occurs in such large numbers, and so closely massed, that several hundred thousand have been taken in a seine at one draft. Millions are taken by ships sent out from New England coast towns. During the last few years, however, especially in 1926, the menhaden have appeared in considerably less numbers, but even in that year enough were caught to yield four million gallons of fish oil, valued at $1,750,000. In 1925 were made six million gallons of fish oil valued at $6,000,000 and $5,600,000 worth of fish meal. As may be expected, the menhaden has to furnish food for many of the other fishes. From the stomach of a single shark have been taken one hundred menhaden. In 1880 Dr. Goode of the Smithsonian Institution in Washington estimated the number of menhaden eaten by predacious creatures of the sea at a million million of millions. The menhaden serves also as a source of food supply for dolphins and porpoises, which are mammals.

Included in and related to the herring family are the *true sardines* and *anchovies*, which are largely caught in the Mediterranean Sea. These fish are somewhat like minnows, since they never grow large. Our native "sardines," as already stated, are really small herring.

THE SALMON FAMILY

The salmons form the finest family of fishes, both as to gameness from the sportsman's point of view and as to shape, color, and appearance. Just as a racing yacht is

superior in design and shape to the ore steamers of the Great Lakes, so the fishes of this family are superior in shape, color, and appearance to most other fishes. Another name for this species might be

Courtesy New York Forest, Fish and Game Commission

FIG. 136. *The lake herring*

"trout," the name given to the smaller and more highly colored members of this fine family. For beauty, activity, gameness, quality of flesh, and sometimes even for size, the salmon rank first among fishes.

The whitefish. The common whitefish, also called *hump-back* or *bowback*, is the best known of this genus or tribe of the salmon family. The last two names denote the shape, the first one the color of this valuable food fish, which is found in the Great Lakes and the waters of adjoining regions. It lives in deep water except at spawning time, which is from October to December, when it comes to shallow water. In the spring there is another movement of the whitefish which is not well understood. The fishes average in weight from one and a half to six pounds, but some weighing twelve pounds have been caught. The whitefish is the second most important fish of our inland fisheries. In 1926 ten million pounds were taken. The wholesale taking of this fine food fish would soon lessen their numbers to the point of vanishing, if it were not for the work of the Fish Commission. In 1926 it collected five hundred million whitefish eggs, which were hatched and the young fish placed in the waters from which whitefish are taken.

Here should be mentioned the lake herring in various varieties, called *cisco*, *bloater*, *tullibee*, and *blackfin*. The smelt also belongs in this family. Lake herring are the most abundant of the food fishes found in the Great Lakes. In 1926 nineteen and a half million pounds of them were taken. This is more than the amount of whitefish taken, but the

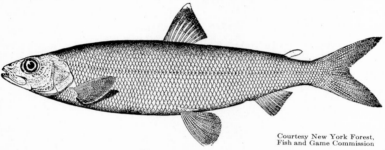

Courtesy New York Forest,
Fish and Game Commission

FIG. 137.   *The cisco*

value is much less. The only drawback of the lake herring is its small size, which is from eight to twelve inches. Although these fish look much like herring, they really are whitefish and the name "cisco" is therefore to be preferred to that of "lake herring."

The salmons.   In swiftness of action, in gracefulness of outline, in gameness and fighting qualities, and also in voracity and dash, the salmons stand supreme. They are found on both sides of the North Atlantic and Pacific oceans and therefore are well known in Europe and also in Asia.

The common or Atlantic salmon, named *Salmo salar* by Linnaeus, the great Swedish naturalist, is the one common to both Europe and America. This fish ascends the rivers both of the Old and the New World. It is well known in

the Rhine and in other rivers of Germany, England, and
Russia, as well as in our New England States, New Brunswick, Nova Scotia, Quebec, Labrador, and even in Greenland and Iceland.

The most famous salmon rivers on our side of the Atlantic
are the Restigouche in New Brunswick and the Saguenay
in Quebec. The Saguenay is the deepest river in the world,
soundings having been made to a depth of five thousand
feet. This stream is simply a river filling out some deep
gashes in the face of the globe. It flows into the St. Lawrence River from the north. On either side of its mouth,
like a huge sentinel on guard, stands a gigantic rock a
thousand feet high. These rocks are called Cape Trinity
and Cape Eternity—surely a romantic setting for the fishermen who are pitting their wits against the wiles of this
glorious game fish found in the Saguenay.

Salmon spend most of their life in the ocean. After
several years of life in salt water they ascend the rivers
flowing into the Atlantic and Pacific to spawn. Spawning
takes place in the autumn, and even earlier, but thousands
upon thousands of salmon begin their upstream journey in
the spring, and the procession is kept up all summer. In
certain rivers of Maine they are known to run up in the
spring, not so much to spawn as to feed on the smelt which
are then ascending these rivers to spawn. While ascending
rivers salmon are so impetuous and agile that they leap over
such obstructions as rocks and rapids, and over dams and
waterfalls as high as twelve feet. "There is nothing in the
water that surpasses a grilse—a young salmon of from two
to six pounds in weight—in its symmetrical beauty, its
brilliancy, its agility, and its pluck," writes an ardent
fisherman.

FIG. 138. *Two salmon*

After Brehm

In the east there are also two landlocked varieties which probably ages ago at very high water got into certain lakes and then when the water fell found their way out cut off. These are the *Sebago salmon* of the lake of the same name in Maine and of other near-by lakes, and the *ouananiche* (wȧ-nȧ-nēsh′) of the Lake St. John region in Quebec. In a rapturous apostrophe the pastor-poet-sportsman, Henry Van Dyke, calls the ouananiche "the noblest, most high-minded fish, the cleanest feeder, the merriest liver, the loftiest

leaper, and the greatest warrior of all creatures that swim."
The Atlantic salmon reaches a large size.   The largest one
ever caught weighed eighty-three pounds, but the average
weight of those taken today along the Maine coast is about
ten pounds.

The Pacific salmon.   Our Pacific salmon are represented
chiefly by five species.   These are the *blue-back, sockeye,* or
red salmon; the *quinnat, chinook, king,* or *spring salmon;* the
coho or *silver salmon;* the *humpback* or *pink salmon;* and

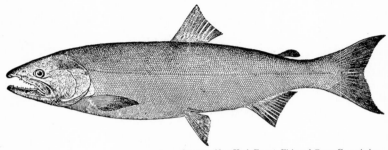

Courtesy New York Forest, Fish and Game Commission
FIG. 139.   *The king salmon*

the *chum, keta,* or *dog salmon.*   Of these the sockeye, weighing from three to seven pounds, is preponderant in the
Fraser River in British Columbia.   The king salmon is
found chiefly in the Columbia and Sacramento rivers.   It
grows to a great size, some weighing a hundred pounds
having been caught.   Specimens weighing sixty and forty
pounds are more common, while the average weight of this
salmon is twenty-two pounds.   The silver salmon leads in
Puget Sound, and weighs from three to eight pounds.
The humpback, weighing from three to six pounds, and the
dog salmon, from ten to twelve pounds, occur in all rivers
along the coast north to Alaska and as far west as Japan.

All these salmon grow to maturity in the ocean. When they are three to five years old they ascend streams entering the ocean. Apparently they do not live far from the mouths of these streams, and when the rivers pour in their waters swollen by spring freshets, or the cold waters from the melting snow and ice on the mountains, the salmon, attracted by this icy water, swim into it and up into the rivers. This movement of the salmon may wane or keep up, becoming stronger in the summer and autumn, for the

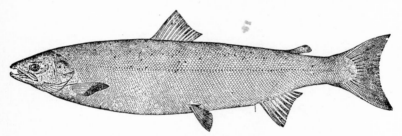

Courtesy New York Forest, Fish and Game Commission

FIG. 140. *The Atlantic salmon*

spawning time of the salmon is from late in August until early in December.

As the salmon ascend the rivers, a remarkable change comes over them. They become red in spots or over large parts of the body. At the same time the scales are absorbed in the skin or scraped off in places, and their jaws even become curved and hooked, so that they cannot be closed tightly. They grow pugnacious and fight together, sometimes to the death. Thus they proceed up the rivers, leaping the rapids and waterfalls, until they reach the smallest brooks at the headwaters of the streams, when they can go no farther on account of the shallowness of the water. Here the water is ice-cold, since often it flows directly from

11

underneath some glacier, and here the male with his tail and snout will dig a hole from one to four feet deep in the sand or gravel. In this hole the female—they are always paired—deposits the rather large eggs, over which the male deposits milt or sperm. Then they are covered over with gravel. This spawning goes on for several days, during which time the males fiercely attack other males that come near. After the spawning is over both the males and the females die. Thus their one spawning trip, their honeymoon, is at the same time their funeral procession. It now seems that some of the young males, the grilse, mate with adult females and after spawning return to the ocean.

Courtesy Am. Mus. Nat. Hist.

FIG. 141. *A salmon leaping*

The eggs hatch in from one hundred and twenty to one hundred and eighty days. At first the young salmon have a yolk sac on the lower part of the body, but this is gradually absorbed, much as is the tail of the tadpole when it changes into a frog. The young salmon stay in the streams a year or two and grow rapidly. Then they enter the ocean, where they live two or three years until the spawning impulse sends them inland into the streams to their death.

During their passage up the Columbia River, which is the principal salmon stream, as well as up all the rivers north as far as Alaska, man takes heavy toll of their numbers. Along these rivers are located large salmon canneries which employ many men, chiefly Indians, who do nothing but catch salmon for weeks or even months at a time. The canneries even have mechanical contrivances, such as fish wheels, which throw out large masses of beautiful salmon automatically. The coastwise steamers cruising north to Alaska in summer are heavily freighted on their return trips with huge piles of crates containing thousands of cans of salmon. Each case holds forty-eight one-pound cans or ninety-six half-pound cans. In Alaska there are one hundred and thirty-two salmon plants, which put out six and two-thirds million cases of salmon in a season, valued at $46,000,000. Add to this the output of the Pacific coast states—Oregon, Washington, and California, with fifty-one plants turning out yearly 835,000 cases, valued at $10,000,-000—and we must realize that enormous though their numbers are, these fine fish may go the way of the bison unless ways and means are found to check or regulate organized greed. Why should a few business corporations be allowed to waste or wipe out valuable natural resources for the gain of a small number of men? Witness the ruthless destruction of our beautiful white-pine forests. Luckily, the Bureau of Fisheries is on the watch and we can trust this efficient organization to put a check to this wholesale organized slaughter of salmon before it is too late.

The most bloodthirsty fish. One would hardly expect to hear that the most bloodthirsty of all fish is a relative of the noble salmon or the trout. Yet this is true. This bloodthirsty fish is the piranha (pĕ-rän'yä) or piraya (pĕ-rä'yä), also called caribe (kä-rē'bä), of South America. It is a veritable fiend, a nightmare to the people living along the rivers which it inhabits. It is not because of its size that the piranha is so greatly feared, for it is not a large fish. But what it lacks in size it more than makes up in unbelievable fierceness. Travelers in South America, as for instance Humboldt, Bates, and Roosevelt, all have had

After Brehm

FIG. 142.   *The piranha*

stories to tell of this fish.   If a little blood is shed in a river
where the piranha abounds, thousands of these fishes immediately swarm about where a moment before none were
visible.   If pieces of flesh are dropped in, the water around
the boat is at once churned up by the fierce rush of these
little monsters.   Their body, which measures only a foot or
a foot and a half in length, is deep and round, much like
that of our sunfish.   Their nose is blunt, and the mouth
full of sharp, strong teeth.   Piranhas are so voracious and
bloodthirsty that they attack any living thing that is moving in the water, even the crocodile.   The sight, scent, and
taste of blood seem to fill the piranha with a frenzy that
nothing can resist.   By their sheer impetuosity, quickness,
and great numbers they can tear to pieces bit by bit a dog,
a tapir, or even a horse before one fully realizes what is
happening.   Even man is not respected by them.   There
are on record many instances of a man in bathing or wading
being attacked and killed by these fish before he could reach

shore.   Many Indians living along piranha-infested streams show ugly scars and wounds made by these diabolical fishes.

THE TROUTS

Trout.   In many ways trout are much like salmon, as they are members of the salmon family.   They are beautiful in shape and color, being marked with red and yellow dots on a dark background.   The food of the smaller trouts usually consists of insects, such as grasshoppers, flies, moths, and butterflies that drop into the water; the larger ones are more omnivorous.   Trout live only in clear, fresh, cold streams.   Here they usually take up their station in the deeper pools, as, for instance, at the foot of a rapids, and hide themselves under a root or a shelving rock.   When they see an insect drop into the water they rush at it with great swiftness, often jumping clear out of the water.   For, like the salmon, they too are great jumpers.

In the northeastern part of our continent are found the *brook* or *speckled trout* and the fine *Great Lakes trout*.   The West, however, is the most favored place for trout.   This is not to be wondered at when we consider the abundance of clear mountain streams and lakes.   Here are found the magnificent *steelhead trout*, the beautiful *rainbow trout*, the good-looking *Dolly Varden trout*, and the *cutthroat trout*. These are all such splendid fish that the Federal Fish Commission and also fish commissions of several states have long considered it a good plan to make the western species of trout available to the East and the eastern species to the West.   As a result one may now catch rainbow trout in the eastern streams and brook trout in some of the western; the steelhead trout may now be caught in the Great Lakes, and the Great Lakes trout in some of the western lakes.

Courtesy N. Y. Zoölogical Society

FIG. 143.   *The steelhead trout*

The California rainbow trout is spreading in Newfoundland, Nova Scotia, and Lake Superior.

Besides all these native trout, certain private or public fish culturists have even introduced some of the best European trout, such as the *Loch Leven trout* from Scotland and the *Von Behr* and *brown trout* from Germany.   All of these imported trout may be caught, among other places, in certain trout streams of northern Wisconsin, where there are also several native eastern and western varieties.

The Great Lakes trout. This magnificent fish, also known as *lake trout*, is the largest of all the trout.   It attains a length of several feet and a weight of sixty to a hundred pounds, the average weight, however, being from about six to twenty pounds.   It is the most important food fish taken in the Great Lakes, although the lake herring or cisco exceeds it in quantity but not in value.   In 1926 no less than eighteen million pounds of Great Lakes trout were caught, a level that had been maintained for ten years.   It is found from the lakes of Maine and New York, through

Courtesy N. Y. Zoölogical Society
FIG. 144. *The Great Lakes trout*

the Great Lakes, up to the headwaters of the Columbia and Fraser rivers in Washington and British Columbia. These trout have a good chance to increase in size and weight, because they live largely in the same waters as the slower, good-natured whitefish, upon which they fare sumptuously. But even the swiftest and bravest fish are no match for their dash and swiftness.

How voracious they are can be seen from the following instances cited by the veteran naturalist, Dr. S. A. Forbes of the Natural History Survey of Illinois, in his excellent book, *Fishes of Illinois:* "A twenty-pound trout caught off Beaver Island in northern Lake Michigan had thirteen herring or ciscoes in its stomach.

"They are as omnivorous as the codfish," says Goode, "and among the articles which have been found in their stomach may be mentioned a seven-inch open jackknife, tin cans, rags, raw potatoes, chicken and ham bones, salt pork, corncobs, spoons, silver dollars, a watch and chain, and, in one instance, a piece of tarred rope two feet long.

Most of this débris was doubtless taken while the fish were following steamers."

I myself have seen the Great Lakes trout and the *red trout* in a lovely little lake nestling among the Laurentian Hills in Quebec, Canada, greedily devour the offal from the kitchen of a summer lodge, when thrown into the water at the edge of the lake. Perhaps these are only exceptional cases.

The spawning season of the Great Lakes trout begins in September, its height being reached in November. Each female deposits five or six thousand eggs.

The brook trout. The game fish most beloved by many anglers, and more written about than any other, is the *brook* or *speckled trout*. The well-known author-sportsman, Henry Van Dyke, lets his enthusiasm rise to pinnacles of praise when he writes of this lovely species. The brook trout wants cool, clear, and clean water to live in. It is therefore found only in our northern states and in Canada, and southward to Georgia in the mountain streams of the Alleghenies. It disdains prairie waters as being too muddy and sluggish. A list of the fishes of Illinois does not contain its name. In the creeks and brooks of Wisconsin, Michigan, New York, the New England states, and Canada, lined with alder, birch, spruce, and hemlock as they are, this speckled beauty is at its best. There it will lie in wait under a root or rock for some luckless moth or grasshopper to fall into the water, for which it rushes with incredible swiftness. This habit is taken advantage of by the fly fisherman, who wades along the edge of the stream, and while remaining hidden himself, deftly throws his artificial fly into a likely looking pool at the end of a small rapids.

Brook trout, according to the waters they inhabit, vary in length and weight from a few inches and a few ounces

FIG. 145. *The eastern brook trout*

Courtesy N. Y. Zoölogical Society

FIG. 146.   *The rainbow trout*

to eighteen inches and several pounds.   Some have been
caught weighing four, six, and even eleven pounds.   That,
in fact, is the common size and weight of trout found in
such rivers of northern Wisconsin as the Brule and Name-
kagon.   In the same waters may be caught the western
rainbow trout, running up to sixteen pounds, as well as
large-sized Dolly Varden, Loch Leven, and European
brown trout.

I know of a small brook in northern Ontario, meandering
through pastures, where in a short time one can catch a
mess of speckled trout six to eight inches long.   This brook
rises in cool, shaded, swampy woods and where formerly
along its course were stands of evergreens and birch are now
fields and meadows.   Thus we see that the brook trout can
adapt itself somewhat to changing conditions, for it is a
hardy species.   From a larger stream in Quebec which I
know, one may pull out brook trout weighing one and two
pounds with angleworms on the hook, something, however,
which a regular trout fisherman would not think of doing.

Unfortunately, many of our streams that formerly harbored this lovely trout no longer do so. They have become so contaminated by sewage and the waste from manufacturing plants that they are hardly fit even for catfish or carp to live in, let alone for the clean-living trout.

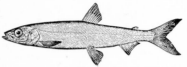

Courtesy New York Forest, Fish and Game Commission

FIG. 147. *The smelt*

We should help the Izaak Walton League and similar public-spirited organizations in their work for the preservation and restoration of our birthright, the unpolluted streams, lakes, and woods of our Great Outdoors.

The graylings. To the trout group belong the graylings, the most famous of which is the *Michigan grayling*.[1] The graylings have the same slender shape as the trout but in general appearance remind one more of the herring. They are found in the cold northern streams in both America and Europe. Bishop Ambrose of Milan, Italy, who lived in the fourth century, called the grayling "the flower of fishes." The Montana grayling, growing from ten to twelve inches long and from a half pound to a pound in weight, is a prime favorite with western anglers. The grayling has beautiful rose and pink marks and dots on the fins and elsewhere.

THE SMELTS

Smelts. The smelts are similar to the graylings in elegance of shape and coloring. They are really marine fishes, but they enter the rivers and lakes for spawning where they sometimes become landlocked. Thus one variety of the smelts is abundant in Lake Champlain and in other lakes and

---

[1] This fine species has now disappeared from the waters of Michigan, even though the Fish Commission of the state made desperate attempts to reintroduce and save it.

rivers from New England to Nova Scotia. The smelt has
now been introduced into the Great Lakes.

In 1622 Captain John Smith, writing about smelts, said:
"Of smelts there is such abundance that the Salvages
(savages) doe take them up in the river with baskets like
sieves." In their abundance smelts remind one of the shad.

THE CAVE FISHES

Blind fish. In many caves, especially in Mammoth Cave,
Kentucky, is found the blind fish of Mammoth Cave. It

FIG. 148. *A cave fish*

has eyes, but they do not
function — that is, the fish
cannot see with them, for
they are concealed under the
skin. Since these cave fish live in absolute darkness, sight
would be of no use whatever to them. Another result of
living in utter darkness is that these fish are colorless. The
blind or cave fish is from two to five inches long.

THE KILLIFISHES

Top minnows. Near Cary, Illinois, on the Fox River, a
winding canal was dredged through a swamp to make sum-
mer-resort real estate. The canal meanders away from the
river and then back to it. There is no current whatever in
it. Here, and in similar quiet waters, you may often see
little groups of tiny, minnow-like fishes swimming, always
in a leisurely fashion, on top of the water. From above
they look brownish gray, like most minnows, but when you
take them out a surprise awaits you. Instead of being
slender-bodied like minnows, these tiny fish are deep-
bodied like bass fry. Their broad, little chubby sides, with
narrow bluish bars running up and down, shine like bur-
nished silver. The eyes are large, and the tail fin is large

and round.   This fish is one of the top minnows, of which
there are several species.   Small though these top minnows
are, they are useful out of all
proportion to their size, for
where they live there are few
mosquito eggs and wrigglers.
It is for these pests among
others that top minnows look
on and near the surface of
the water.   Unfortunately,
these tiny fish are so delicate
that it is almost impossible
to get them to an aquarium
alive.   They are about two
inches long.

FIG. 149.   *Two top minnows*

One of the top minnows,
ranging from Illinois to Maryland and south to Texas, is

FIG. 150.   *The mud minnow*

viviparous, that is, its young are brought forth alive.   In
the tropics there are many kinds of top minnows, doubtless
because there are even more mosquitoes there than here.
Many of these tiny fellows are highly colored, usually
scarlet, and are therefore imported by dealers in aquarium
supplies.   Many of them are also viviparous.

THE MUDFISHES

Mud minnow.   When seining for specimens for an aquarium, one often gets the mud minnow.   When seen for the
first time, the mud minnow might be taken for a young
trout, although the stagnant, muddy nature of the water
where it is usually caught should at once dispel any such
belief.   This minnow is of about the same shape as the
trout and, like that fish, it is also marked with brown and

pink spots, even the fins being pink.   Far from belonging
to the trout family, however, it belongs to the family of
mudfishes.   Unlike the top minnows, it is always found
at the bottom of prairie pools, never in running water.   It
is therefore easily kept in an aquarium, where it is a real

FIG. 151.   *Two pikes*
Upper, a common pike; lower, a grass pike

ornament.   But a mudfish that I once kept in an aquarium
had the bad habit of now and then jumping out.   The
mud minnow is from three to four inches in length.

THE PIKE FAMILY

The pikes.   The fishes of this family have an elongated
body, not very deep, with the back forming a straight line.
The dorsal fin is small and is placed far to the rear, near the
tail.   The mouth is very large and full of teeth, even the
tongue being studded with them.   The lower jaw is larger
than the upper.   Pike are extremely voracious, darting at
anything that remotely resembles something edible.   Often

they will dart at and swallow a bare spoonhook that is trolled behind a boat. They lurk among the plants on the bottom of ponds, lakes, or rivers, looking out from under the leaves for any prey, be it fish, frog, or insect, sometimes seizing even small ducks and muskrats. What they get they swallow at one gulp, and are then immediately ready for another meal. Their flesh is good, although it cannot be compared in flavor with that of the trout or salmon, and besides it is rather full of bones. Often, because of its habitat in mud-bottomed lakes or rivers, it has an earthy, mucky taste.

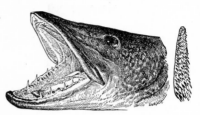

After Schmeil

FIG. 152. *Head and palate of a pike*

The pickerel. The smallest members of the pike family are the pickerels, also called *grass pike*. In coloring they are olive green, with many curved dark lines. They can be distinguished from the pike by the fact that both cheek and gill covers are scaled, whereas in the pike the lower half of the gill covers is bare. The pike is also larger, growing to be three to four feet

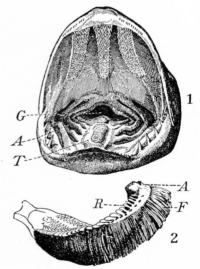

After Schmeil

FIG. 153. *Gills of a fish (pike)*

1, front view of open mouth; 2, one of the gill arches of a whitefish. *F*, gill filaments; *A*, gill arch; *G*, gullet; *T*, tongue; *R*, gill rakers, for straining the water.

long, while the pickerels measure from one to two and a
half feet. The largest pike on record was one taken in Fox
Lake, Illinois, which weighed thirty-three pounds.

The muskellunge. The largest fish in the pike family is
the muskellunge, an Indian name spelled in many different
ways, such as *muskellunge, muskallunge, maskalonge.* In
this fish the cheeks and gill covers are scaleless. It attains
a length of eight feet and a weight of a hundred pounds, the
record weight being one hundred and eight pounds. Such a
size and weight are, of course, only exceptional. As a game

Courtesy New York Forest, Fish and Game Commission
FIG. 154. *The muskellunge*

fish the muskellunge is a great success, putting up such a
stubborn fight that it takes much skill and endurance to
land one. When it has taken a bait and hook it leaps out
of the water again and again in its efforts to shake out the
hook. With its huge head and open jaws, this great fish
presents an almost terrifying appearance. What a terror
it must be to the other fishes in its chosen haunts!

The muskellunge makes its home in the larger lakes in
Wisconsin, Minnesota, and Canada, and in the Great Lakes.
In some Wisconsin lakes it is very dark, almost black in
color, while in others it is almost pink or brassy.

Farther south and east is found another muskellunge,
the *Chautauqua* or *Ohio muskellunge.* It lives largely in the

lake from which it gets one of its names, and here five-foot specimens have been caught. Formerly this muskellunge was found in the Ohio River at Louisville and Evansville, but in the last decades it has become rare.

THE EELS

The common eel. The eels are the most snakelike of fishes. The head is conical, the mouth small, and the lower jaw a little longer than the upper. The scales are so small and so imbedded in the skin that most people think eels have none. The gill opening is small, and next to it is a small pectoral fin. The dorsal fin is narrow but long, extending from the middle of the back to the tail and around it, where it unites with a similarly long anal fin.

Although the eel was known to the ancients, its life history remained unknown until quite recently. Not until about 1900 did we learn how and where eels reproduce. It is now known that the common eel, when several years old, runs down the streams to the ocean, thus being *catadromous*. Only in the ocean waters do the eggs in the female develop; that is why eggs are never found in eels caught in fresh water. The number of eggs produced by one female is enormous, up to about ten million. After the spawning is over, the adult males and females die, just as do the salmon. Like salmon and shad, they do not feed while migrating. At other times they are voracious. The eels of Europe have been found to go to the neighborhood of the Bermuda Islands to spawn, those of North America to the Bahamas.

"On their hunting excursions," writes Ballou, "they overturn alike large and small stones, beneath which they find species of shrimp and crayfish, of which they are excessively fond. Their noses are poked into every imaginable hole

12

in their search for food, to the terror of innumerable small fishes."

Eels are largely scavengers, eating dead fish and other dead animals found in the water. A dead horse in a river is likely to be full of them, a meeting place, as it were, for all the eels of the neighborhood. They are an annoyance to commercial fishermen in lakes and rivers, because they devour the fish caught in their gill nets. Sometimes at night eels may even be found prowling around among the

FIG. 155.   *The fresh-water eel*

vegetation on shore. In Europe they are suspected of raiding vegetable gardens, as they are supposed to have a great fondness for peas. Since frogs have been found in their stomachs, perhaps that is what they are stalking on their nightly forays. At any rate, it is certain that eels can live out of the water for a considerable length of time.

At first young eels are transparent little things, quite different from the adults. In this larval stage they are called *elvers*. But after a few weeks they assume the shape and appearance of the adults and try to migrate up into the rivers. Millions upon millions of young eels may then be seen at the foot of Niagara Falls. Over less high falls they somehow manage to squirm. Being sticky and clammy, it is possible for them to crawl over nearly perpendicular surfaces. Although millions of them may perish in the attempt, the rest, still many in number, use the dead bodies of their comrades to help them over the obstacle. Since eels are able to leave the water and glide through dewy grass, perhaps in this way they may get around rapids and falls. Is it not wonderful that the young eels should be able to find the way from their spawning grounds, without the guidance of older fish, back to the rivers of Europe and America?

After Brehm

FIG. 156. *The electric eel*

The common eel sometimes becomes four to five feet long, but the average length is from two to three feet. In winter eels bury themselves in the mud at the bottom of rivers and ponds and hibernate, or at least become nearly inactive.

The electric eel. A rather dangerous kind of eel, the *electric eel*, is found in South America. Here it is neighbor of the terrible piranha. Between these two fishes, man or beast would have a poor chance of escaping unharmed. The electric eel grows to be from five to six feet long. It has no scales or dorsal fin, but a long anal fin. The small mouth is armed with many sharp teeth. But its principal weapon of offense does not consist of its teeth, but of the strong electric battery contained in its body. The great scientist and explorer Humboldt tells how he could hardly persuade Indians to catch a few of these eels for him, even when he offered them large rewards. Finally, he had them drive some wild horses into an eel-infested stream in order to weaken the electric batteries of the eels. A lively scene

After Brehm

FIG. 157. *A flying fish*

ensued. The horses writhed in agony in the river, some fell down and got up, but two were not able to rise and were drowned within five minutes of the time they had been driven into the water. The others, frantic and partly paralyzed by the discharges of the numerous eels, tried to make for shore, but were driven back by the Indians. After the batteries of the eels had thus been weakened, the Indians were willing and able to catch them.

After the eels have fully discharged their stored-up electricity, they are inactive for a time and cannot give a shock. The electric organs occupy about four-fifths of their body. Another scientist, Walsh, was able to produce an electric spark from an electric eel. These eels are naturally terrible enemies of the other fishes, upon which they prey. By means of their powerful electric discharges they kill more fish than they can eat, thus helping to deplete the waters in which they live. Even turtles and crocodiles try to get away from the neighborhood of these eels.

THE FLYING FISHES

Flying fishes. The flying fishes, of which there are many species, have narrow, herring-like bodies. They are peculiar in having much elon-

Courtesy Am. Mus. Nat. Hist

FIG. 158. *A tropical Atlantic flying fish*

gated pectoral fins. When pursued by one of their many enemies, they swim with great speed, and then if not able to escape will launch themselves into the air. With the momentum gained under water, they are able to sail through the air for a distance varying from a few rods to an eighth of a mile. The ventral and also the caudal fins are then held rigid, but the pectorals vibrate. Whether this is done to produce motion, as is the vibration of birds' wings, or whether it is due simply to the impact of the air on them, coupled with the speed at which they go, is a debated question. The truth seems to be that they do both. They glide through the air from the impetus gained by their rapid swimming before leaving the water, and when in the air they help to sustain themselves there and stay up in it longer by deliberate movements of the fins. When the fins are dried out, the fishes have to drop back into the sea, often to be swallowed by the grim enemy that has followed below in the water.

There are about fifty kinds of flying fishes, most of them living in the warmer seas. They vary from a foot or less to a foot and a half in length. Often flying fishes, during their aërial stunts, land on the decks of ships. The sailors rarely return them to the water, but keep them, as they are very good eating.

FIG. 159.   *The climbing fish*

After Brehm

THE PIPEFISHES

Pipefishes. These peculiar fishes certainly live up to their name, for they resemble nothing so much as animated pipes. Their body is slim and pipelike and their mouth also is elongated into a pipelike organ. Thus, they resemble the gars of the fresh waters. The pipelike effect of their body is heightened by a cord or whiplike appendix, about as long as the body, which grows from the center of the tail. This is probably

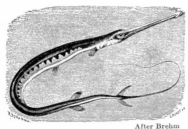

FIG. 160.   *The pipefish*

After Brehm

to make them look still more like the seaweed among which they live. Among this seaweed in the ocean—their only habitat—they move either horizontally or vertically.

Besides their peculiar shape, the pipefish possess another startling feature. They resemble not only the gars but also in a way the kangaroo. Just as the kangaroo mother places her underdeveloped young in a pouch of skin on her abdomen,

so the pipefishes carry their young in a similar pouch.
Only in their case it is the male that has the pouch, which
is formed by two flaps of skin on the underside of the tail.
In this pouch the female de-
posits her eggs, and here they
hatch out. Thus the male
pipefish has to serve as a living incubator. It is even
asserted by some that later,
when the young are in danger,
the father fish opens his pouch
so they can disappear within
it and be safe.

After Schmeil

FIG. 161. *Head of a seahorse*
(enlarged)

The gill cover has been removed to
show the gill bundle.

The seahorse. Related to
the pipefishes is the curious
little seahorse, which gets its
name from the resemblance
of the outline of its head to
that of a diminutive horse.
In spite of this, however,
its mouth is somewhat pipelike. The seahorse's tail, also
pipelike, is unlike that of any
other fish, and in addition is
prehensile—that is, it can be
used to take hold of things.
Thus it can twine its tail
around the stem of a seaweed
and there rest or look for some-

After Schmeil

FIG. 162. *Seahorses among the*
seaweeds

thing to eat. That is what the seahorse is doing most of
the time, as it is a very feeble swimmer. The seahorse is
found along our eastern coast from Cape Cod to Florida.

It reaches a length of six inches, but some kinds in other parts of the world grow to be a foot or more long. The young are hatched out in the sac of skin on the underside of the tail of the male, as in the pipefish.

THE STICKLEBACKS

If one is fond of nature and wishes to observe some of the most interesting life processes, he cannot do better than keep an aquarium. An aquarium may be made highly

FIG. 163. *The brook stickleback*

instructive as well as a thing of beauty and a joy forever, although it does require a great deal of work.

A pugnacious fish. Once I added to my aquarium several sticklebacks which, together with other small fishes, I had caught in a pond with a fine-meshed seine. The sticklebacks were about two inches long. One had nine spines on the back, without any membrane between them, the others five—although some sticklebacks have as many as fifteen spines. The eyes of these fish were large. Their color was a dark olive, with black curved lines over it. It was amusing to see how rigid they became the moment some little movement attracted their attention, keenly eying the object of their suspicion, or how they darted about with the greatest speed. But my pleasure over these lively, spiny little fellows was soon changed to apprehension and then to dismay, for they soon began to dart after the other fishes and nip their tails, until their victims became sorry looking objects. There was nothing to do but to remove the trouble makers.

Thus it can be seen that sticklebacks are pugnacious, and always full of fight. They are also voracious and greedy for food. Had the other fish in the aquarium been a little

After Schmeil

FIG. 164. *The nine-spined stickleback and its nest*

smaller than the sticklebacks, they would all have been eaten up. Once a stickleback kept in an aquarium devoured in one hour seventy-four young dace, a quarter of an inch long. Usually, however, the sticklebacks seem to live mostly on small crustaceans and insects

Sticklebacks show their fighting disposition most at mating time, especially when they build and protect their nest. To speak of building a nest sounds strange in connection with a fish, but that is precisely what the stickleback does. It is the male, not the female, which builds the nest out of bits of wood and pebbles, fastened among water plants. The nest has two openings. The male forces the female to enter the nest and deposit the eggs, after which he enters to deposit his milt. Then he guards the nest jealously, and woe to any fish, large or small, that dares to come near! As the kingbird drives away all other birds from near his nest, so the stickleback will dart at any fish approaching and bite and pursue him until he has put some distance between him and the nest.

FIG. 165. *The great barracuda*

The sticklebacks are northerly fishes, being most abundant from New York northward to Greenland and very common in Canada and Newfoundland, although several varieties range as far south as Kansas.

THE BARRACUDAS

A fish to be feared. If one were to make a list of the fiercest and the most dangerous and voracious fishes, the barracudas would stand among the first on the list. Especially is this true of the great barracuda of our eastern coast and the warmer parts of all oceans. Along our coast this fish reaches a length of six feet, but travelers among the South Sea Islands say that there it attains a length of twenty feet. The natives of these islands fear it much more than they do the sharks. Even the smaller barracudas are so voracious that sometimes they do not hesitate even to try to bite a chunk out of some bather. Wherever something is stirring, suddenly and silently like a grim spect will appear the long flat shape of a barracuda. They loo like destroyers too, for they resemble the pike and muskellunge in shape and large size of head and jaws. They

FIG. 166. *The brook lamprey*

are, however, even better equipped than those killers, inasmuch as they have two dorsal fins instead of one, and even larger teeth. Both commercial and amateur fishermen on the Florida coast take especial delight in catching these monsters of the deep as well as the sharks. Needless to say, no fisherman ever returns one alive to the sea. It is now caught and canned as a food fish.

THE REMORA OR SUCKING FISH

Fishes that do not swim. Just as boys, when there were more wagons on the streets than now, would jump on the back of one and get a "free ride," so is there also a fish that steals a ride. Only this fish does not steal a ride in sport but for entirely different considerations. This is the *remora* or *sucking fish*, which has on top of the head an elliptical sucking disk composed of a double row of movable cartilaginous plates.

After Brehm

FIG. 167. *The remora*

This disk enables the remora to attach itself to sharks, tunas, tarpons, or any other large fish and also, no doubt, to such small whalelike mammals as the dolphin and the porpoise. Thus they spend much of their life in getting "free rides." This they do not in order to explore all the various parts of the ocean, but to get from one feeding place to another. Since the remora does not swim by its own exertion, it has no air bladder.

The remoras must not be confused with the *lampreys*, which are not even considered as fishes, but are classed just below them. The body of the lamprey is eel-like, but its mouth turns downward, somewhat like that of the sucker. Its mouth is round and full of teeth. Lampreys also attach themselves to the bodies of other fish, rasping a hole into the body and sucking out blood and shredded flesh. Thus they are parasites of the worst kind. If they stay long enough on a fish they will finally bore their way far enough in to destroy the vital organs. One kind of lamprey is found in the North Atlantic, while others are found in the rivers and lakes of the United States and Canada.

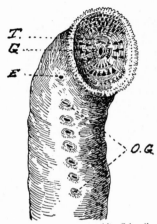

After Schmeil

FIG. 168. *Fore part of the body of a lamprey, with open mouth*

T, the so-called tongue; *G*, opening into the gullet; *E*, eye; *OG*, openings of gills.

THE SWORDFISH AND THE SAILFISH

The swordfish. The swordfish gets its name from the swordlike prolongation of its upper jaw. This bony sword, however, is flattened horizontally, not vertically. The dorsal fin of the swordfish is very long—a foot or more— and often may be seen cutting the surface of the water without any part of the body of the fish being visible. This is another monster fish, attaining a length of fifteen feet

After Brehm

FIG. 169.　*The swordfish with its prey*

FIG. 170. *A sailfish*
Notice the huge dorsal fin and the narrow, sickle-like pelvic fins.

and a weight of eight hundred pounds.   The swordfish is
common in the warmer seas, as around Florida, and is found
even as far north as Nova Scotia in Canada.   It is becoming
an increasingly important food fish off the New England
coast.   In 1926 two and a half million pounds of swordfish,
valued at $500,000, were taken there.

Instances are recorded of swordfishes charging a boat
and piercing the planks or timbers to a length of ten to
twenty inches.   If, as is asserted, these monsters also attack
other large fishes and whales, their "sword" certainly is a
powerful weapon.   The swordfish is said to follow schools
of herring, mackerel, and menhaden, rise into their midst

from below, and strike out right and left until he has killed enough to make him a meal.

The sailfish. Judging from appearances, the sailfish should be a first cousin of the swordfish, and so indeed it is. The sailfish also has a sword, but it is much shorter than that of the swordfish. To make up for this, however, its backfin is a good deal higher, which gives the fish its name. The "sail," violet in color and about two feet high, is truly a huge affair. At Florida resorts the sailfish at present is a special attraction, for all tourists seem to have an ambition to catch one. This fish follows the Gulf Stream northward as far as Cape Cod, but not in such numbers as does the swordfish. The two pelvic fins are long and narrow, like two knives. They can be folded back into a long slitlike opening in the abdomen, into which they fit like a sword in its scabbard.

THE MACKERELS

The common mackerel. The common mackerel must be ranked next to the herring as a food fish in numbers caught, in size and number of its schools, and in the range and length of its migrations. While similar in size to the herring, the mackerel has an even finer shape, being more tapering forward. In its graceful outlines this fish reminds one of a racing yacht. It has a larger mouth than the herring, which means that it is more voracious; then it has two dorsal fins instead of one, which denotes that it moves at greater speed than does the herring. In color, too, and in markings it surpasses the herring. It is silvery with a blue line running along the center of each side, upward from which run many wavy blue lines to the back, making the mackerel an unusually handsome fish.

Fig. 171.   *The mackerel*

The common mackerel is found in the North Atlantic from Cape Hatteras to Newfoundland and across to Norway and Spain.   Like the herring, it is a highly migratory species. It appears on our eastern coast in the spring, traveling north, where it remains during summer.   In the autumn it is again on the move, but exactly where it goes nobody knows.   Mackerel schools when in migration are enormous. In 1848 was seen a school a half mile wide and over twenty miles long—an almost solid mass of mackerel.   It was estimated that another school seen off Block Island would yield one million barrels of fish.   In 1926 the catch of mackerel of the New England fishing fleet amounted to thirty-four million pounds, valued at $1,300,000.

Mackerel feed on small crustaceans and other fish, such as herring, menhaden, and anchovies, and are in turn eaten by larger fish, such as the cod and bluefish.   They are also preyed upon by dolphins and porpoises.   Mackerel are prolific—a large female containing as many as a million eggs, which hatch out in five days in water of a temperature of fifty-eight degrees.   This is a short hatching period compared with that of the salmon, which is one hundred and eighty days. Other fishes have a hatching period of eight or ten days.

The bonito. Another well-known mackerel, the bonito, found only in warm seas, is a highly esteemed food fish in the South. It attains a length of four feet. Beside these

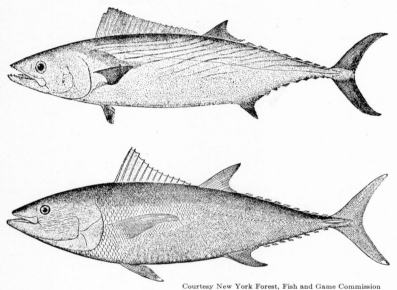

Courtesy New York Forest, Fish and Game Commission

FIG. 172. *Two members of the mackerel family*
Upper, the bonito; lower, the tuna fish.

the *Spanish mackerel*, the *club mackerel*, and the *kingfish* belong to the mackerel family, all fine food fishes.

The tuna, tunny, or albacore. The tuna, the giant among the mackerels, attains a length of fifteen feet and a weight of fifteen hundred pounds. This, however, is exceptional. It is found in all warm seas from the Mediterranean to Newfoundland and Florida and in the Pacific, especially

13

around the Santa Barbara Islands. On the Atlantic coast the tuna is often called *horse mackerel*, and chasing the tuna is now just as popular on the coasts of Maine and Florida as it has been at the Santa Catalina resorts. It seems unbelievable that a fish weighing hundreds of pounds can be caught with hook and line, but that is true of the tuna. Naturally, it takes exceptionally well-made tackle and an uncommon degree of skill, daring, and patience to land such

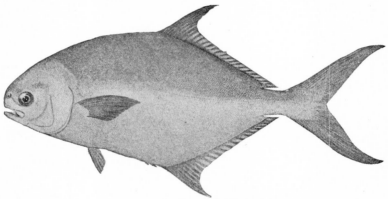

Courtesy New York Forest, Fish and Game Commission

FIG. 173. *The pompano*

a giant. Often the boat of the fisherman is dragged miles away from the spot where the fish was hooked, out toward the open ocean, which is not any too safe for small craft. A tuna weighing two hundred and fifty-one pounds was long the largest one caught with hook and line, but of late still larger ones have been secured. Zane Grey, the well-known writer, once landed a tuna weighing six hundred pounds. After having been pulled and jerked about for hours, the successful angler for these monsters finally succeeds in getting his prey up close to the boat, where it is

From *American Food and Game Fishes.* Copyright 1902 by David Starr Jordan and Barton Warren
Evermann, and reprinted by special permission of Doubleday, Doran and Company, Inc., publishers

FIG. 174. *The bluefish*

speedily dispatched with the gaff. In 1926 no less than
five hundred thousand cases of prepared tuna were packed
in California.

The *pompanos*, belonging to a family related to the
mackerels, are prime favorites as food fishes in the South,
where their flesh is considered a great delicacy. They are
from eighteen to thirty-six inches in length.

THE BLUEFISH

A destructive fish. Here we may need to revise our
opinion as to the most voracious and ferocious fish afloat.
So far as destructiveness to other fishes goes, the bluefish
probably ranks first. Professor Baird, formerly head of the
Smithsonian Institution of Washington, states that there
is no parallel to the bluefish in point of destructiveness to
other fishes along our coasts. This fish seems to be an
animated "chopping machine, the business of which is to
cut to pieces and otherwise destroy as many fish as possible
in a given space of time," says David Starr Jordan. Bluefish not only kill enough for their own use, but much of the

time they seem to kill without reason.   Like wolves, bluefish travel and hunt in packs, only in far larger packs.   Where a pack of bluefish has made its way the trail is marked by pieces of fish sinking in the water and by blood stains. If a fish is too large for them to swallow they simply bite off the rear part and let the rest sink to the bottom.   It is even asserted by some that when the stomach of these gluttons is full, they disgorge the contents and begin killing and gorging all over again.

It has been estimated that in a single season there are a thousand million bluefish on our eastern coast.   Each fish is supposed to eat at least ten other fish a day, or more than its own weight.   That makes ten thousand million fish devoured by these bluefish in a day.   For one hundred and twenty days they linger on our shores, which makes the bill of fare for their whole stay twelve hundred thousand million fish.   This shows what an almost inexhaustible reservoir of life the ocean is.   It also shows how important it is that some species of fish, such as menhaden, alewives, mackerel, and mullets, should occur in almost incredible numbers.

The bluefish is an extremely well-built and strong fish, resembling trout in its appearance.   It usually weighs five or six pounds, but some weigh as much as fifteen pounds, while a record bluefish tipped the scales at twenty-two pounds.   Many are caught for food, as their flesh is firm and well flavored.

THE BASSES AND SUNFISHES

This is one of the best-known families of fishes, for in it are found some of the finest of all game fish.   In most of these fishes the body is short, compressed, and rounded, so that they are almost round in outline.   Since they are all carnivorous they are, therefore, well equipped with teeth and fins. Their mouth is turned upward. They have large dorsal and anal fins, the forward part of the dorsals having spiny rays, and the rear part soft ones. These fish all breed in the spring, most of them making nests in the sand or gravel, which they defend with courage.

The crappies. The crappies belong to the sunfish family. Over most of their range two kinds are found—the *white* and the *black crappie*, which is also called *calico*, *grass*, and *strawberry bass*. Crappies attain a length of twelve inches, and together with the black bass they are the best game and food fish in the sunfish family. Their flesh is firm, white, and sweet. The white crappie is mostly silvery in color, with dusky bars coming down

FIG. 175. *White and black crappie*

FIG. 176. *The rock bass*

over the sides from the blue back. The black crappie is similar to the white except that instead of bars it has numerous black spots on a greenish-white ground. Even the large fanlike dorsal, caudal, and anal fins are spotted in both species. Crappies are found in the more sluggish waters from the Great Lakes to Texas and Kansas. Annually from eight hundred thousand to one million three hundred

thousand pounds of them are caught by commercial
fishermen in the upper Mississippi valley alone. From the
Illinois River two hundred and ninety-four thousand
pounds have been taken in some years.

Similar to the crappies in
shape and size is the *rock
bass*, also called *red-eye* and
goggle-eye, because of the red
iris in its eye. It is olive
green, the brassy-colored
sides being much mottled
with dark green. The rock
bass lives in ripples among
rocks, as well as in muddy-
bottom streams.

The sunfishes proper. Sunfishes are well known to most
boys, because they take the
plainest hook, but poorly

FIG. 177. *Two sunfishes*
Upper, bluegill; lower, green sunfish.

hidden by an earthworm, more readily than the trout
takes the most elaborate fly. They are noted for their
rotund outline, their high colors, and their hardiness in an
aquarium. One must, however, keep sunfishes alone in an
aquarium, because if other small fish, such as minnows, are
also kept in it, they will soon disappear down the capacious
gullets of the sunfishes.

The *warmouth bass* is a sunfish that makes an attractive
aquarium species. It is olive green, with brassy sides
spotted with bluish, greenish, and copper red. This bass
reaches a length of ten inches.

The *green sunfish* is another beauty. As its name implies,
this fish is green with a brassy luster, each scale having a

blue spot with gilt edgings, while the fins are largely blue.
This fish, which grows to be seven inches long, is common
in small brooks.

Of all sunfishes the *bluegill*
or *blue sunfish* is probably
the best known. Like the
warmouth bass, it is olive
green, but has no red on its
fins. Old specimens are often
dusky with a coppery red
belly. The name "bluegill"
comes from the color of the
rear lobe or flap of its gill covers. In most waters bluegills

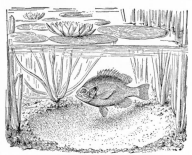

From *Parental Care among Fresh-
Water Fishes*, by Theodore Gill
FIG. 178. *A common sunfish
on its nest*

grow to a length of eight inches, but in some lakes they
attain a length of twelve to fourteen inches.

The *pumpkinseed* or *common sunfish* is one of the best
known of this family. It is of a greenish olive in color, with
bluish sides and belly and the lower fins of orange.

The most highly colored of all sunfish is the *orange-spotted
sunfish*. All the colors of the rainbow seem to show on its
sides, red and orange being especially prominent. Since
it is a small fish—only three and a half inches long—it is
ideal for the aquarium. The colors of this and of all other
sunfishes are much brighter at breeding time, which is in the
spring, than at any other time.

The black bass. In the sunfish family belongs the black
bass, a fish which many fishermen hail as the king of American game fishes. There are two varieties of black bass, the
large-mouthed and the *small-mouthed*, the latter being the
preferred one. Both are green or olive green in color,
mottled with black, but can be distinguished easily by the

size of the mouth.   Moreover, the dorsal fin is more deeply
notched in the large-mouthed bass than in the small-
mouthed.   "The black bass," says J. A. Henshall, in his
Book of the Black Bass, "is eminently an American fish; it
has the faculty of asserting itself and of making itself completely at home wherever placed.   It is plucky, game,
brave, and unyielding to the last when hooked.   It has the
arrowy rush and vigor of the trout, the untiring strength
and bold leap of a salmon, while it has a system of fighting

FIG. 179.   *The large-mouthed black bass*

tactics peculiarly its own.   I consider it inch for inch and
pound for pound the gamest fish that swims."

The large-mouthed bass is larger in every way than the
small-mouthed.   In its northern range it reaches a length
of two and a half feet and a weight of from eight to nine
pounds.   I have seen one weighing nine pounds, taken in
a lake in northern Indiana, but its usual weight is from two
to three pounds.   In Florida bass weighing fourteen pounds
have been caught.   Here there is almost no winter and the
fish therefore can be active and feeding the year round and
thus put on greater weight.   The range of the *straw bass*,
as the large-mouthed bass is also called, is wider than that

of the small-mouthed bass. It extends from the St. Lawrence, the Great Lakes, and the Red River of the North
to Florida, Texas, and northern Mexico, while the range of
the small-mouthed bass is from the same northern boundary
only as far south as South Carolina and Arkansas. It is
also more discriminating as to the waters it inhabits, pre-
ferring deeper and cooler waters than those inhabited by
the large-mouthed bass. As cold weather approaches, the
small-mouthed bass hibernates, which means, in the case of

FIG. 180. *The small-mouthed black bass*

a fish, that when winter comes it goes into deep water and
there leads a half-dozing existence, eating little or nothing.

In the spring, however, the small-mouthed black bass
shows redoubled energy. The male is one of the most
energetic nest builders among fishes. He builds the nest
in about three feet of water, digging with his snout into
the sand or gravel of the bottom and meanwhile fanning
away with his tail, the sand and mud that he stirs up. After
he has dug down three or four inches he stops. The sand
has formed a ridge around the hole, or else a piece of wood or
a log lying on the bottom forms a partial protection. The
female is not even present during the nest building, which
takes from four to forty-eight hours. When the nest is

completed the male forces or coaxes the female into it, where she deposits her eggs in several successive spawnings. Then she is chased away and the male stands guard over the nest. He will dart swiftly at any fish, large or small, that dares come near his treasure.

It takes about six years for the small-mouthed bass to attain a weight of three pounds; after that a half pound is added yearly until the maximum weight of six to seven pounds is reached. As a matter of fact these large old fellows are rarely caught, for they have learned the wiles of the fishermen.

The small-mouthed bass is not sought by commercial fishermen but the large-mouthed one is to some extent. Thus in the Illinois River as many as a hundred thousand pounds are caught annually. Although these are both good food fish, their flesh is surpassed by that of the trout, whitefish, crappie, perch, and even by that of some catfish. It is not for their flesh, however, that the real angler seeks the black bass, but because of their fighting qualities, gameness, and great rushes and jumps when hooked. Both varieties are likely to jump five or even six feet up out of the water.

THE PERCHES

The yellow perch. In summer, in vacation time, when one walks along the lake shore of Chicago he will find the edge of breakwaters, docks, and jetties lined with boys and girls, as well as with men and women. They are all sitting patiently with their legs dangling over the water, each one intently watching the cork on a line which he is holding over the water. All are angling for the *yellow perch*. And the yellow perch, like the catfish, is accommodating enough to

allow himself to be caught with the simplest of fishing
outfits.   In fact, the yellow perch is so voracious and greedy
that any kind of bait will attract him.   Sometimes while
fishing in some of the Canadian lakes we got among a school
of perch so eager to snap at anything thrown into the water
that occasionally we caught one on a bare hook.   It was
possible in a short time to secure from fifty to seventy-five
perch with nothing more elaborate than a plain hook and
a worm.   The perch probably has the sweetest tasting flesh

FIG. 181.   *The yellow perch*

of any fish, but it is much smaller than some other game
fishes, being usually only from ten to fourteen inches long
and weighing from a half pound to one and a half pounds.
The perch is a beautiful fish.   Its back is dark olive and
its sides golden yellow, with six to eight broad, dark cross-
bars running from the back down below the middle of the
sides.   The lower fins are orange, the upper ones somewhat
olive in color.   The dorsal fin is very spiny.
The distribution of the perch is a northerly one, ranging
from the Great Lakes west to the Red River basin, thence

north to Hudson Bay, and from there south through New
England to the Neuse River in North Carolina. It spawns
in April and May, and, like the toad, deposits its spawn in
the form of ribbons.   Once a perch in an aquarium in Washington deposited a ribbon eighty-eight inches long.   The
commercial catch of perch in Lake Michigan, which in 1899
amounted to six hundred and seventy-seven thousand
pounds, had in 1926 risen to over seven million pounds.

The wall-eyed pike or pike perch. This admirable food
and game fish gets its names "wall-eye" and "glass-eye"

FIG. 182.   *The wall-eyed pike*

from the white iris of the eyes, which gives it a peculiar
staring appearance, somewhat as if it were blind.   Otherwise it is a beautiful fish, dark olive mottled with a brassy
or golden color, although the sides are sometimes entirely
golden.   This is the reason the French in Canada call it
doré, meaning "golden."   This perch grows to be three feet
long and is an excellent food fish.   It is found from the
Great Lakes northward, being most common in Canada.
The catch of wall-eyed pike in the Great Lakes in 1926
amounted to twelve and a half million pounds.

The Great Lakes fishermen, especially those of Lake
Erie, divide pike perch into two classes, which they call
blue pike and *yellow pike*.   But these are either color

variations of the wall-eyed pike or else represent different ages of this fish. The *sauger* or *sand pike* of the Great Lakes is, however, an additional species of pike perch.

The darters. Closely allied to the perches are the *darters*. These fishes have the same two semicircular, fan-shaped dorsal fins as the perches, but the body is smaller and narrower in outline. Because of their slimness and small size—about two and a half inches long—these darters might easily belong to the minnow family. But their appearance and actions at once betray their relationship to the perches. Darters live in rapidly flowing creeks, usually among pebbles and stones on the bottom.

FIG. 183. *Three darters*
Upper, black-sided darter; middle, Johnny darter; lower, darter.

The best known and most interesting member of this family is the *Johnny darter*, which is often caught as one seines for aquarium specimens. When placed in an aquarium it at once attracts attention by its peculiar behavior. It always remains at the bottom, resting on its pectoral fins, which it uses like arms or legs. As a result the forward part of its body is bent upward. From this peculiar position it watches intently with its big eyes all that is going on above and around it. If anything arouses its suspicions it darts with great rapidity to some other spot, perhaps under a stone or plant.

The darters feed on the larvae of water insects, notably those of the May flies, and on small crustaceans. The males of several species of darter, as for instance the *Iowa darter*, are highly colored. Other darters are the *banded*, the *sand*, the *green-sided*, the *fan-tailed*, and the *black-sided darter*, all desirable aquarium species.

THE SEA BASSES

One summer four of us made a trip along the Atlantic coast of Maryland. In a so-called catboat, navigated by

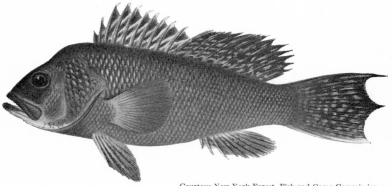

Courtesy New York Forest, Fish and Game Commission

FIG. 184.   *The sea bass*

a native of the region, we threaded our way through the innumerable channels among the many mudflats and islands between the mainland and the open ocean. At night we always made for a life-saving station or a lighthouse, where invariably we were cordially received by the captain and the crew. The stations that stand out most prominently in my memory are those at Smiths Island, Hog Island, and Cobb Island. Upon our arrival the station cook would immediately get busy and prepare a sumptuous

meal, which when set before us vanished like snow in an
April sun.   Fish, usually *sea bass*, was the chief dish at these
memorable meals.   That was my introduction to this fine
fish.   If one has the idea that ocean fish are not quite so
fine in flavor as fresh-water fish, he still has a surprise await-
ing him.   Those sea bass certainly were delicious.   The
men at these stations had fish boxes at their little wharves
in which they kept live fish of several kinds.

Varieties of sea bass.   The *striped bass, rock fish,* or *rock*
is one of the sea basses.   This fish, which reaches a length

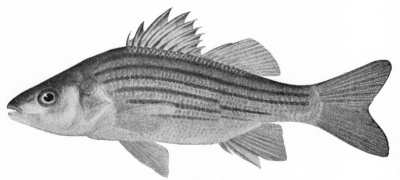

FIG. 185.   *The yellow bass*

of from three to five feet, is found from Nova Scotia to
Louisiana.   It gets its name from its lengthwise stripes.
Captain John Smith waxed eloquent about this fine fish,
which is plentiful.   Near Norfolk, Virginia, fifteen hundred
striped sea bass have been taken with one haul of the net.
At another time six hundred were taken, each fish averaging
eighty pounds in weight.   This fish is of an olive silvery
color with seven to nine blackish stripes.

The *yellow bass* also belongs to this family, although it
is a fresh-water species.   This fish inhabits large rivers and

lakes and is found in the lower Mississippi River and north to St. Louis and Cincinnati, also in a few lakes and rivers of northern Indiana, such as Tippecanoe, Eagle, Pike, Center, and Chapman lakes, in Kosciusko County, and in the Eel River at Logansport. It is found in the Illinois River as far up as Ottawa. The yellow bass reaches a length of from twelve to eighteen inches, and a weight of from one to five pounds. It is brassy yellow or olive buff,

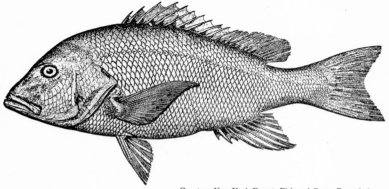

FIG. 186. *The red snapper*

with sometimes as many as seven lengthwise stripes on each side of the body.

The *white bass*, which also belongs to the sea-bass family, is found in large rivers and lakes. This is a beautiful fish, silvery in color, tinged below with golden and with narrow dusky lines on its sides. It occurs from the St. Lawrence River to the Great Lakes, where it is most numerous, and thence west to Manitoba. Thus it is more northerly in its distribution than the yellow bass.

Another sea bass is the so-called *white perch* which, unlike the white bass and the yellow bass, is found in the ocean as well as in fresh water. Dr. David Starr Jordan pronounces the white perch the best flavored of all fishes after the yellow perch. It is olive in color, with silvery sides. It is found along the Atlantic coast from Nova Scotia to South Carolina, and in rivers entering this part of the ocean.

Still another toothsome fish belonging to the bass family is the *red grouper*, handsome both in color and form. This fish, which is common in the Gulf of Mexico and adjacent waters, attains a length of three feet.

The red grouper must not be confused with the *red snapper* of the same waters. This fish reaches a length of from two to three feet. It is a beautiful fish, and agreeable

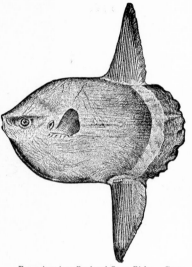

From *American Food and Game Fishes.* Copyright 1902 by David Starr Jordan and Barton Warren Evermann, and reprinted by special permission of Doubleday, Doran and Company, Inc., publishers.

FIG. 187. *Mola or headfish*

to the taste. With improved methods of icing and refrigerator-car transportation, the red snapper is now sold in New York and Chicago as well as in New Orleans.

Finally, we must mention the *jewfish* or *black sea bass*, a giant even among the many great fish found in the ocean. Try to imagine a small-mouthed black bass enlarged to a length of six feet and a weight of three hundred and fifty pounds, and you have the jewfish. It is common in the Gulf of Mexico as well as in the Pacific around the Santa Barbara Islands, where the tuna, not to mention sharks,

14

rays, and even whales, also disports itself. Once on the
Gulf coast I saw an angler pull out a jewfish weighing
ninety-six pounds—a small fish as jewfishes go.

Thus we see that bass are really oceanic fish; our fresh-
water bass are only sunfish.

THE HEADFISH OR MOLA

The mola. Standing on the beach at Atlantic City, or
anywhere else along the Atlantic or Pacific coast, one may

FIG. 188. *Sheepshead or drum*
The one living in fresh water.

sometimes see a large silvery object, disklike in shape,
floating on the surface of the water some distance out from
shore.   If one looks more closely, he will discover that there
is a big fin moving lazily through the air above the disk.
This is none other than the unique *headfish* or *mola*, also
called *sunfish* from its habit of thus sunning itself.   If one
of these fish is pulled ashore it presents a most amazing
spectacle.   It seems to be nothing but the huge head of a
large fish which has been cut off from some giant fish and
left swimming about.   The headfish attains a gigantic size,

the largest one on record being eight feet, two inches long, with a weight of eighteen hundred pounds. This is not a food fish, but if one is caught it is sometimes converted into fish oil.

THE SHEEPSHEAD OR DRUM

The sheepshead. The *sheepshead, drum,* or *croaker* is a large coarse-fleshed fish found in the Great Lakes and in the waters to the north and south. Like the buffalo fish, it is humpbacked and attains a length of three and even four feet, and a weight of from fifty to sixty pounds. Both male and female produce a drumming sound, which has given it the names "drum" and "croaker." Whether or

Courtesy N.Y. Zoölogical Society

FIG. 189. *The sheepshead or drum*
The one living in the ocean.

not this sound is made with the two small, round pebble-like bones in their head is hard to tell. Some people think it is produced by the vibration of the walls of the air bladder, which in turn is caused by the contraction of special grunting muscles. Related fishes that go under the names of drum, croaker, and sheepshead are found in the ocean. The last named is considered one of the best food fishes in New Orleans.

THE CODFISH FAMILY

The cod. One of the most important food fishes on our side of the Atlantic is the cod. Codfishing has grown to be a very important occupation on our northeastern seaboard, six hundred vessels and seven thousand men being employed in this industry. The cod is not caught with nets but with

Courtesy American Museum of Natural History

FIG. 190. *The cod*

handlines baited largely with fish and squid, and fished for from small boats, or from the deck of larger vessels.

The cod is most plentiful on the continental shelf off the New England coast, and especially on the Grand Bank of Newfoundland. The Basques in Spain claim that their ancestors knew of the cod fisheries on this side of the Atlantic before Columbus ever set sail on his eventful journey. They even assert that a Basque told Columbus about them. It was because of the profitable codfishing that England proclaimed Newfoundland her first colony. For the same reason, when France was compelled to give up her whole North American empire in 1763 after the French and Indian War, she held out for the possession of at least two small islands off the coast of Newfoundland. France still owns St. Pierre and Miquelon in these waters. Another kind of cod is found in the North Pacific and in Bering Sea.

The average size of the codfish caught varies from twelve to thirty-five pounds, but one six feet long, tipping the scales at two hundred and eleven pounds, has been taken. The cod is a very prolific fish. A twenty-one pound specimen has been computed to contain two million seven hundred

thousand eggs, one of seventy-five pounds nine million one
hundred thousand eggs.   If all these eggs were to hatch and
the young live, and in turn thus multiply, the ocean would
soon become a solid mass of cod.

This fish is omnivorous, eating crustaceans, mollusks,
and other fish.   Even water plants have been found in its
stomach.   Like the herring and the mackerel, the cod is
migratory, but its movements are not well understood.   It

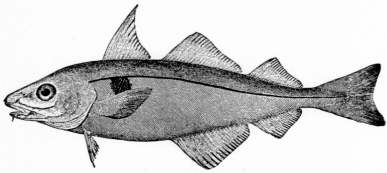

Courtesy New York Forest, Fish and Game Commission
FIG. 191.   *The haddock*

is a deep-water fish, being found usually in water of a depth
of from one hundred to one hundred and fifty feet.

The color of the cod varies from greenish and brownish
to yellow and even reddish, with many brown spots on the
sides and back.   The United States Fish Commission does
its best to keep up this important fishery.   Up to the year
1898 it had set out five hundred million cod fry.   In 1927
the commission secured no less than six billion cod eggs for
propagation.   In that same year the catch of cod amounted
to the huge total of forty-seven million pounds, valued at
about $1,750,000.   On the Pacific coast nearly five million
big and handsome cod were caught in the same year.

The haddock. The *haddock*, a close relative of the cod, is also a valuable food fish. This fish feeds mainly on mollusks, that is, snail-like animals. Those caught usually

FIG. 192. *Heads of young flounders*
This drawing shows the moving of the one eye to the side
which is to become the upper side of the fish.

average from three to four pounds in weight, although now and then one weighing up to seventeen pounds is taken. In 1927 no less than ninety million pounds of haddock, valued at $3,000,000, were taken. Most of this catch is frozen and shipped over the country, thus enabling the people far inland to obtain marine fish practically fresh. Lately, however, much of the haddock catch has been salted, smoked, or dried. Smoked haddock goes under the name "finnan haddie."

Other cods. The *pollack* or *pollock*, averaging three feet in length, is another member of the cod tribe, as are the *hake* and the *cusk*. A single female of these varieties produces as many as four million eggs.

THE FLOUNDERS OR FLATFISHES

The flounders. The flounders are unique among fishes. A change so astonishing as to be unbelievable goes on in the life span of each individual in this family. When a flounder first emerges from the egg it is like all other fishes, swimming upright and having a symmetrical head with an eye

on each side.   But soon a remarkable change takes place.
The young flounder begins more and more to swim on one
side of its body—that is, it holds itself more and more horizontally in the water.   Then its
bodily development is gradually
adapted to this unusual position.
The eye which is on the under
side in the horizontal position begins slowly to move to the top of
the head and then to the other
side, where the other eye is located.   The bones of the head,
too, adapt themselves to this new
position.   Finally the fish swims
only on one side, both eyes now
being on the upper side.   The lower surface becomes color-

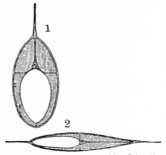

After Schmeil

FIG. 193.   *Cross section through
body of (1) a carp and of (2) a
flounder or halibut*

less, while the upper side gains in color.   Who would believe
such a thing possible?   Yet it is an actual fact.

The halibut.   The halibut is the best known of all the
flounders, at least to landlubbers, as seamen call all people
living inland.   It is also one of the largest fishes, weighing
three hundred to four hundred pounds, and sometimes even
more.   A halibut weighing three hundred and fifty pounds
usually measures from seven to eight feet in length and
nearly four feet in width, flounders of such size, however,
being the exception, not the rule.   The male is much
smaller than the female, a condition true in many species
of fish.   The back fin of the flounders extends from the head
to the tail, and the anal fin from the tail to the head.   But
since these fishes no longer swim upright, their fins look
more like a fringe around the fish than like fins.   When
waiting for prey, halibut partly bury themselves in the sand

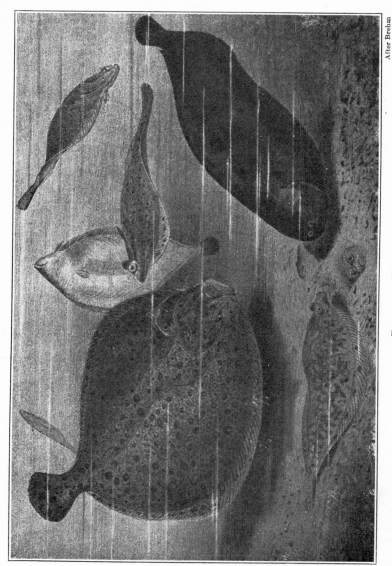

FIG. 194. *Flatfishes*

or mud on the bottom of the sea, where they can look upward without themselves being seen.

How important the halibut is as a food fish may be seen from the following figures. In 1926 four million pounds of halibut were brought into the ports of Gloucester and Boston, Massachusetts, and of Portland, Maine, and two and a half million pounds to the ports on the Pacific coast in Alaska, Califorina, and Washington. Most of the Pacific catch of halibut, cod, and other fish is sent across the country to eastern markets. The halibut is found in all northern seas.

After Brehm

FIG. 195. *A puffer fish, called porcupine fish*

Other flounders have such descriptive names as *window pane*, *sole*, *tongue fish*, and *flatfish* or *winter flounder*.

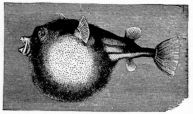

After Brehm

FIG. 196. *Another puffer fish*

THE SWELLFISHES OR PUFFER FISHES

Puffer fishes. On the tables of souvenir dealers in Florida may often be seen a dried, globular, spiny fish. This is the *porcupine fish*, so called from its spines. The globular, bubble-like shape is not the usual one of this fish. When swimming about peacefully it looks more like a little prickly bass, or similar fish. When an enemy comes along, however, the porcupine fish immediately inflates its stomach until it becomes globular. Then, should an enemy fish try to seize

one, it will simply bounce up and down like a toy balloon.
The teeth of these curious fishes seem to have run or melted
together into the long, thin tooth found in each jaw. Some
of the puffer fishes have no spines, but all are very rough.
One of these fishes found in Asiatic waters is made into
lanterns by the Japanese.

THE ANGLER OR ALLMOUTH

The allmouth. We should like to close our account of the
fishes with a sketch and picture of a very beautiful fish.
But according to the systematic arrangement we have followed we must close with one of the ugliest of fishes. Although there are several species of anglers, we shall consider
only the most important one, which is designated by such
names as *fishing frog*, *bellows fish*, and *allmouth*. This monster of ugliness has been termed the owl among fishes, but
that is really an injustice to the owl.

Imagine a flat, rough, brown creature, three to six feet
long, which, much like the tadpole, seems made up only
of head and tail. Then imagine a truly gigantic mouth,
and you have the angler. It owes its name to the fact that
it seems to angle for other fishes. For this purpose the forward dorsal fin consists of several long spines, which stand
upright. The first spine, which is the longest or highest,
leans forward over the head and has a flap of skin at the
upper end. The monster lies on the bottom of the ocean
where it is shallow. Here it can hardly be distinguished
from its surroundings, because its color blends into that of
the sand, mud, rock, or seaweed. The angler may even dig
itself into the sand or mud, so that only its mouth and eyes
are exposed. Most fish are extremely curious, and anything out of the ordinary attracts their attention. Seeing

this little flap of skin waving in the water, a fish will at once lower itself to inspect it more closely. Suddenly the cavernous mouth rises up from beneath the flap and the curious fish is engulfed. The angler's stomach is as capacious as is its mouth. Dr. Goode once saw an angler pull a loon under the water (a loon ordinarily is about thirty-six inches long and weighs about ten pounds). The stomach of one angler contained seven ducks, in another were found six coots or mudhens, in another were found seventy-five herring, while in still another

After Brehm
FIG. 197. *The angler or allmouth.*

were twenty-one live flounders. In each case that meant only one meal.

The angler lives in the ocean, but in May it enters bays to spawn. And the spawning is as peculiar as is the creature itself. The eggs are deposited by the female angler in the form of a ribbon of jelly-like material thirty to forty feet long and from four to five feet in width. Each one of these "veils" contains about one and a third million eggs. At this rate there should at all times be plenty of anglers in the ocean, for if the young are as unattractive looking as the adults, few other fish should have an appetite keen enough to swallow any of them.

SUGGESTIONS FOR THE TEACHER

ARTHUR E. DIESING

Silent reading of factual material plays an important part in life. Modern readers offer too little of such material. Some training in this type of silent reading is acquired in the so-called content subjects. This valuable ability must, however, receive more direct attention. Teachers who have felt this need will welcome the publication of *Reptiles, Amphibians, and Fishes*, the second volume of "Our Great Outdoors" series, for it offers worthwhile factual material in a form admirably adapted to this type of work. Besides its intrinsic interest to the child, the material is written in an interesting style and achieves the difficult and rare combination of scientifically accurate information written on the child level.

The following suggestions are designed to aid the teacher in adapting to teaching situations the material offered in this book. The fertile mind of the experienced teacher will see numerous other ways in which he may proceed to meet his own particular conditions and needs. The following may serve as a starting point.

1. Have the children read one of the short selections under timed conditions. Instruct the children to read as rapidly as possible, with the knowledge that they will be held responsible for the facts read. The teacher will write the minutes and seconds on the blackboard, and as soon as each pupil has finished reading he will write on a blank piece of paper the time last written by the teacher. After all have finished reading, they will be given a certain time to reproduce the facts read. Papers may be graded by the teacher or, preferably, by the class.

If the results are not satisfactory, give the children another chance to read the material and then again reproduce it in a similar way.

2. Similar to "1." The teacher will have a list of questions prepared which the children will be asked to answer after their reading. It is a good plan to have these questions duplicated, and distributed to the children after their reading, or they may be written on the blackboard.

3. Similar to "2," but let the children know the questions before they begin to read. (For the technique of setting questions and grading, see any of the modern silent reading tests.)

LANGUAGE

1. The teacher may read one of the selections. The children will be asked to reproduce the material.

2. A better type of composition work would be to have the children read the material themselves and get the facts, which they will be asked to rearrange under some topic or problem. Vary the types. Gather the material from a single article or from several articles on one topic. Write a composition from experience after reading an article. Write a composition based upon experience, developing it from the imagination. Try some from imagination entirely. The following topics may serve as examples:

Usefulness of Snakes
The Feeding Habits of Snakes
Protective Coloration
Wrong Notions concerning Snakes
How to Treat a Snake Bite
A Personal Adventure with a Snake
Frogs I Have Seen (identify and describe after reading section
    on frogs)
The Truth about Toads
Adaptation of Fishes to their Watery Home
The Fishing Industry in the United States
The United States Bureau of Fisheries
Misnamed Fishes
Game Fishes

My Most Exciting Fishing Trip
The Fish I Didn't Catch
My First Fish
Fish in Our Neighborhood
Fish Preservation
A Fish Story—Told by the Fish
A Visit to a Fish Market
Fish Products
Interesting Habits of Fishes
Food of Fishes
Feeding Habits of Fishes
The Izaak Walton League
Dangerous Fishes
Spawning Habits of Fishes
Queer Fishes

GEOGRAPHY

Have the children use this book as a reference text when studying the animals of a certain region. The geography text usually does not offer sufficient material to give the child a clear concept.

DRAWING

The reproduction of some of the excellent pictures and drawings contained in this volume may easily, under the guidance of the teacher, lead to an interest in drawing the same animal from nature, in which the child will be encouraged to portray the individual animal, not merely the type. The child may be referred to this book when he asks the teacher's advice as to the detailed drawing of a reptile or fish. The child will learn that frequently an inability to draw is due to a lack of knowledge of the details of the object to be drawn rather than a lack of technique. Have him read the section on the animal he wishes to draw, observing carefully the details, trying out the drawing, then checking up to see whether the details have been accurately portrayed in the drawing.

NATURE STUDY

Wherever possible, the child should be encouraged to visit the zoo and the aquarium to see these animals and to describe some of them to the class.   A class excursion to the zoo and the aquarium will prove a delightful and profitable experience.   Encourage children to take note of these animals in their surroundings and to tell the class about them, giving the individual touches so interesting to children and their experiences with these animals, and stories about them.   A class may decide to make a collection of pictures of these animals.   Aim mainly at arousing the interest of the child in the wonders of nature and whetting his appetite for more, in order that he may develop the desire, habit, and ability to observe the world about him with a greater degree of intelligence and appreciation.   Wherever possible, encourage the child to study animals at first hand and to compare his findings with the information given in this volume, thus leading him to the scientific attitude toward life about him.

THE AQUARIUM IN SCHOOL AND HOME

An aquarium is such a prolific source of pleasure, entertainment, and instruction that it deserves to become much more popular than it is at present. One can then at his leisure and in the pleasant surroundings of his home observe the intimate life processes and activities of many of the smaller inhabitants of the water. In their watery home out in the open these, as a rule, can hardly be seen, let alone observed and studied. An aquarium is a corner or section of nature cut out and transferred to the home or school. In school, of course, the children must be persuaded, or coaxed, or forced to keep their hands off, otherwise the keeping of an aquarium becomes an impossibility.

FORM AND SIZE OF AQUARIUM

What form should the aquarium have? By no means the form of the glass globe so often seen in homes, wherein one or several unhappy goldfish wage a continuous fight against suffocation from want of air. Instead, the aquarium should be as wide at

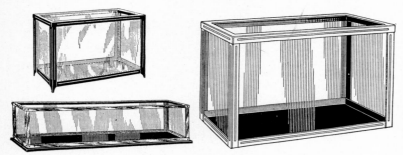

FIG. 1. *Types of aquariums that can be bought from dealers*
The long and narrow shape is designed to fit on a window sill.

the top as possible, in order to allow the air to press on and enter into the water. Therefore the square or rectangular forms are the ones to choose (Fig. 1). The more air has a chance to enter the

15

water, the less danger there will be that it will become foul.   For this reason also the depth of an aquarium should not be too great. The rule is that twenty-four square inches of water surface should be allowed for each inch of body length of fish.   Thus a six-gallon aquarium, which is nine by sixteen inches at the top, has one hundred forty-four square inches of water surface, and will support six inches of fish; a nine-gallon one, thirteen inches of fish.   These thirteen inches should not, of course, be in the form of one fish, for such a fish would be too large for an aquarium, and would tear up the plants and the other contents of the aquarium.

Here are some dimensions for aquariums as now sold by dealers. For window display:

$$28 \times 7 \times 10 \text{ inches} = 9 \text{ gallon}$$
$$40 \times 9 \times 12 \text{ inches} = 18 \text{ gallon}$$

For a standard aquarium, to be placed on a table or stand:

$$12 \times 7 \times 10 \quad \text{inches} \quad = 3 \text{ gallon}$$
$$16 \times 9 \times 11 \quad \text{inches} \quad = 6 \text{ gallon}$$
$$18 \times 11 \times 12 \text{ inches} \quad = 9 \text{ gallon}$$
$$22 \times 13 \times 14 \text{ inches} \quad = 17 \text{ gallon}$$

However, in regard to size one may suit his own fancy and the space at his disposal.   I have seen octagonal aquariums that were very attractive.

How to Make an Aquarium

If a boy is handy with tools, or has an older brother or friend of that type, he can make himself an aquarium.   The frame may be made of wooden angle molding (Fig. 2).   The four upright pieces may be nailed on the corners of a rectangular piece of good strong board (Fig. 3).   The four upright pieces must be connected with molding below and at the top, well mortised or nailed in the corners, because the weight and outward pressure of a number of gallons of water is very great.   The frame must be firm and strong, nothing wobbly about it (Fig. 4).   On the board below

may be fitted a piece of tin plate or glass or, best of all, slate.   If
one has the tools and machinery at his disposal, the frame may be
made of angle iron, well riveted together, with a piece of slate or

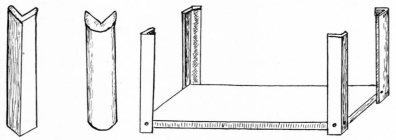

FIG. 2.   *Two types of*   FIG. 3.   *First stage in the construction*
    angle molding   *of the aquarium*
In Fig. 3, notice the projection of the uprights below the board, to allow space
    for the pieces of molding to be nailed to the edges of the board.

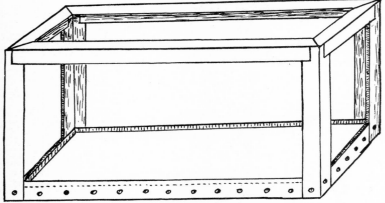

FIG. 4.   *The frame of the aquarium complete*
The dotted line in front shows how far the angle molding overlaps the board.

a piece of plate glass used for the bottom.   The panes of glass
for the sides should not be cut so as to make a very tight fit, as
the resulting tension may later cause a sudden cracking or even
breaking of the glass, with very unlovely results to the room in

which the aquarum is placed.   Before the glass is set in place
a thin layer of one of the following preparations should be laid on
inside of the molding, so that the glass becomes imbedded in it
as well as the slate, tin, or glass used on the bottom.

  a. Roofing tar, brought to the proper thickness by the addition of plaster of Paris.   The tar may be procured from
   any roofer or tinner.

FIG. 5.   *The finished aquarium, showing a part of the contents*

  b. Glycerine and litharge, mixed to the consistency of putty.
  c. Mix two pounds of putty, one-fourth pound of litharge,
   and one-fourth pound of red lead to the proper consistency
   with boiled linseed oil.
  d. Two gills of plaster of Paris, two gills of fine white sand,
   two gills of litharge, and three-fourth gill of powdered
   rosin, mixed with boiled linseed oil.

The chances are that one may obtain some even better cement
or putty by applying to stone-monument makers or similar
tradespeople.   After the glass forming the walls of the aquarium
has been set, more of this cement or tar must be pressed into the

corners and along the edges where the panes meet and be made smooth and even by passing a knife or some other tool over it.

What to Put into the Aquarium

After the cement or putty has been allowed to harden—never pour in the water before the container has become thoroughly dry—you may proceed to equip your aquarium. Clean sand to the depth of about an inch should go on the bottom. Into the corners, or wherever your sense of beauty dictates, put water plants, weighting down the roots or the ends of the stems in the sand with stones to make them stay in place. Plants are necessary to an aquarium, not merely as an added ornament, but mainly as a means of keeping the water from rapidly fouling. Plants give off oxygen, which is used by fishes and other animals in their breathing. The latter exhale carbon dioxide, which in turn is taken in by plants to make their own food, starch, and so forth, for their own upbuilding. Thus if one puts into the aquarium the proper amount of plant material and the proper amount of animal material, a balance will be struck, and the water may be kept in good condition for a long time. How much of each kind of material is needed to strike this balance must be found out by experimentation. Practice makes perfect here as elsewhere.

In the center one may build up a kind of cave or tower of striking looking stone, such as quartz and calcite and their crystals, both as an ornament and as a retreat for those fishes which like to hide.

Plants for the Aquarium

The best plants for the aquarium are eelgrass, water milfoil, various kinds of pondweed (*potamogeton*), the smaller arrowheads (*sagittaria*), water weed (*elodea*), frog's-bit, water crowfoot, or even the beautiful southern water hyacinth, which, however, is likely to be too large for any but very large aquariums. Even the little floating disks of duckweed may be put on the surface from time to time. One should not, however, overstock the aquarium with plants.

Fish for the Aquarium

Goldfish hardly fit into an aquarium kept mainly for instruction. The hardiest and at the same time the prettiest of our native fishes are the sunfishes, to which belong also the black bass and the rock bass. A baby pike may be an interesting tenant once in a while. All these fishes, however, are highly predacious, so it will not do to have minnows, which one wishes to keep, in the same aquarium or in the same compartment with them. For the sake of variety, some of our highly colored and elegantly shaped minnows, dace, chubs, shiners, and stone rollers may be added to the aquarium from time to time. But to do this one must either remove the sunfish and take them back to the creek or river, or have two aquariums, one for the predacious, the other for the non-predacious fishes. Or a screen of metal may be placed in the middle of the aquarium, thus separating the two species.

Other Inhabitants of the Aquarium

An aquarium stocked with fish only would be incomplete, for in nature no body of water has fish only for inhabitants. Baby turtles are found interesting and amusing to watch, and if the eggs of frogs are placed in the aquarium, their development into tadpoles and then in turn into the adult frogs is absorbingly interesting. Other amphibians that may well have a place in the aquarium are the newts, creatures which are rarely seen in nature and therefore are little known. But in an aquarium they can be observed at leisure. The imported red-spotted salamander is even more of an ornament than the newt. Insects, too, may furnish a welcome and interesting addition to its population, a few whirligig beetles gyrating on the surface of the water at once lending an additional touch of nature to the aquarium, while the large, shining diving beetles are interesting in the extreme. A diving beetle I once had in my aquarium would come to the surface from time to time as though it wanted to look around (in reality to breathe), then it would dive again, with a shining bubble of air clasped against its abdomen to provide it with air for breathing in the water below for some minutes. Then it spun a bubble of silk as a receptacle for its eggs, which floated on top of the water.

When seining with a small hand seine for material for the aquarium, one will occasionally get the large larvae, or grubs, of the diving beetle, or of dragonflies, or of the dobson. It is interesting to watch them in the aquarium, as they are extremely voracious, not hesitating to attack tadpoles and even minnows larger than themselves. After a while they change into nymphs, and then into the adult dragonfly or dobson. The larvae of the caddis flies, in their little cylinders of sand or bits of wood, are also interesting objects to watch.

For the sake of completeness, one may occasionally place in the aquarium a small crayfish—commonly called "crawfish"—that would be the clown of the outfit. A large one, of course, would do more harm than good.

Among the most interesting denizens of the aquarium are snails. They are useful also, because they eat the algae that are sure to grow on the inside of the glass. Pond snails of several species, shapes, and sizes may be gathered in almost any pond or swamp (Fig. 6). Some of them breathe under water by means of gills, while others, being lung breathers, are obliged to come to the surface from time to time to breathe. One large imported snail from Asia regularly slides up on the glass and projects a long syphon upward out of the water, to take in a large supply of air. All snails deposit their eggs on the inside of the glass.

Small river mussels—commonly called clams—also make interesting objects for the aquarium. The way they put forward their hatchet-shaped foot, pull themselves up on it, and thus plow through the sand is a revelation to most beholders.

FEEDING THE AQUARIUM TENANTS

The rule for the feeding of the creatures in the aquarium, as in all else in connection with it, is to come as near to nature as possible. All superfluous disturbance of the water and of the

After Baker, *Gastropoda*

FIG. 6. *Pond snails for the aquarium.*

a, limnaea; *b* and *c*, planorbis; *d*, physa; *e*, paludina; *f*, pleurocera. The last two are gill breathers; the others, lung breathers.

inmates must be avoided, and one must guard against overfeeding. In winter especially hardly any feeding is necessary, as the fishes are then sluggish and refuse food, even if the most tempting morsels are placed right before their noses.

For predacious fish, earthworms are a fine food. If small minnows are easily obtainable they make an ideal food, also the most natural. Bits of raw meat or liver are greedily taken, and also some insects, such as flies and their larvae. For minnows, chubs, dace, and shiners, insects and their larvae, such as flies and mosquito wrigglers, are natural articles of diet. For the smaller ones the small members of the crustacean or crab class are the most natural food, such as water fleas (*daphnia*), copepods, such as the cyclops, fresh-water shrimps (*gammarus*), and so on. It may be advisable to keep a small aquarium or a battery jar especially for raising a food supply of these tiny denizens of standing water. When a few plants are placed in such a container, they multiply very rapidly. In fact, they do that in the aquarium itself; no standing water is without them.

Keep the Aquarium Clean

All food not eaten must be removed; otherwise it will decay and make the water foul, although little catfish and crayfish often make themselves useful as scavengers by eating up any overlooked particles of food. Do not remove bits of food with the hands, but with a small dipnet or a long-handled spoon.

Although the plants in the aquarium are powerful agents in keeping the water wholesome, yet the nitrogenous water voided by the fish and the other animals will finally render the sand on the bottom foul. You will notice that the sand, at first white or yellow, will soon take on a blackish gray or even a greenish color, just like sewage. And it is sewage. This foul sand should be removed from time to time by syphoning it out with a small hose kept for this purpose.

If the water seems to be becoming too stagnant, remove half or three-fourths of it with the syphon, and fill up with fresh water. This new supply should be of about the same temperature as that which was already in the aquarium, for otherwise the shock to the animals may be too great.

Once in a while it may become necessary to remove everything in the aquarium, if for no other purpose than to scour off the scum and the algae which gather on the inside of the glass. Remove the fishes with a dipnet. At such a housecleaning all the sand may be taken out, the stones and the whole aquarium scrubbed, and new sand and new plants, if it seems advisable, put in.

Especially does this become necessary when the fish seem to be ailing, and even start to die. When whitish spots or other discolorations appear on the body of the fishes, it is a sign that some small animal or fungous parasite is working on them. Often all that is necessary to remedy the trouble is to take out the fishes and place them in a bath of salt water, using three heaping teaspoonfuls of salt to a quart or so of water. They may be left in this bath a half-hour or longer.

Although I would advise stocking the school or home aquarium with life forms found in one's own neighborhood, or at least in one's own country, yet it must be noted here that many aquarium keepers have long ago branched out into keeping in their aquariums tropical fishes also. These are, as a rule, very interesting on account of their beauty of color and form, as well as for certain peculiar habits they have. Some of these tiny beauties—several are only an inch or so long when adult—bring forth living young; a few species keep the eggs produced in their mouth until they hatch, while at least one kind is able to make a nest for its eggs out of tiny bubbles of water or some other substance. Such tropical species are the gourami, trichopodus, trichogaster, ctenops, chanchito, gambusia, poecilia, danio, pterophyllum, sphenops, and others. Aquariums stocked with such showy species may be called the aristocrats among them. But for them a far more elaborate and expensive outfit is necessary, such as artificial heating of the water, a system of aëration—that is, forcing air through the water continuously—and the like. This takes much money and time, both of which are often not at one's disposal.

THE TERRARIUM

The terrarium is designed to enable one to observe and enjoy small land plants and animals under conditions resembling those under which they are found in nature. The problem here is simpler, because the container need not be so thoroughly watertight as in the case of the aquarium. There are two kinds of terrariums, the wet and the dry.

The wet terrarium, or semi-aquatic aquarium, is one in which moist conditions are reproduced, but not aquatic ones. An old aquarium that perhaps no longer can be made entirely watertight may serve as one. Cover the bottom with sand and soil, preferably humus from the woods, and on this plant or place peat moss and other mosses, also other small bog-loving plants. Wet thoroughly, and a small bog may thus be reproduced. In it one may grow such curious plants as sundew, Venus flytrap, and pitcher plant, all three of which are carnivorous plants, catching and digesting insects. A tight-fitting glass plate must be placed over the top of the container, to conserve the moisture. In this way a miniature botanical garden may be had in the house which is beautiful to look at and at the same time self-perpetuating. By the addition of a few small frogs, tree frogs, lizards, salamanders, turtles, toads, and snails it may become a zoölogical garden as well. Insects in their several stages may with advantage be placed in the terrarium, so that their wonderful metamorphosis or change may be watched at one's leisure and without any hardship. It may be made a thing of beauty and a joy forever.

The dry terrarium may also be made out of an old aquarium, or at least out of the frame of one. If there is none available, get some angle molding and make a rectangular frame much like that used for the aquarium. Only instead of lining it with glass, line it with wire screening. If the floor part can be made watertight it is so much the better. The floor may be made of slate, glass, or galvanized iron, with putty around the margin. It should be covered with sand, gravel, and stones, with some good soil here and there for the growing of small plants to give some concealment or food to the animals. In the center an imitation pond may be made by putting in a pie plate or saucer filled with water, the edges hidden under the surrounding sand or gravel. That will make the terrarium more attractive, and allow the inhabitants to take a bath or drink. The finest members of the population of such a terrarium would be a lizard or two, several horned toads or lizards from Texas, a little box tortoise or two, an elegant little grass or green snake, a ring-necked snake, a red-bellied snake, and a young garter snake. A daddy longlegs and several beetles, butterflies, and snails would make the picture complete. Here also the metamorphosis of insects may be observed under the best conditions.

A GLOSSARY

abdomen, lower part of body

absorb, to suck up, drink in

acrid, sharp, biting

agility, nimbleness

air bladder, a sac lying below the backbone of fishes and filled with air, corresponding to the lungs of higher vertebrates

alimentary, pertaining to feeding

alimentary canal, the food canal through the body

amphibians, cold-blooded or change-able-blooded vertebrates that begin life in the water, but later, in many cases, change to a life on land; they have a naked skin

amputate, to cut off

anadromous, running upstream to spawn, as many salt-water fishes do

anal, pertaining to the external opening, or vent, of the intestine

animation, the life processes taken together; liveliness

anterior, forward, toward the front

aquatic, pertaining to or living in water

auricle, one of the chambers of the heart

automatically, doing something mechanically, machine-like, by itself

barbel, an elongated, fleshy projection on the head of fishes

basking, lying in the sun

batrachians, frogs and other amphibians

buoyant, able to float; floating easily

calcareous, made of or consisting of lime

capacious, roomy, large

carapace, the upper shell of a turtle

carnivorous, flesh-eating

cartilage, gristle; half-bone

cartilaginous, pertaining to or like gristle

catadromous, running down rivers to spawn, as some fresh-water fishes do

cavernous, cave-like; large; spacious

chitin, the hard, horny substance which forms the shell or covering of insects

chitinous, pertaining to or like chitin

denizens, inhabitants

diatoms, tiny, microscopic, one-celled plants living in water

digits, fingers or toes

dilatable, able to be expanded

distensible, able to be distended or expanded

dorsal, pertaining to the back

dorsal fin, the fin on the backs of fishes

elliptical, of the shape of a drawn-out circle

embryo, an animal or plant in its beginning

emit, send out

environment, the surroundings

epiderm, the outer layer of skin

epidermal, pertaining to the epiderm or epidermis

filament, any slender, thread-like structure

fissure, crack

fluke, one of the halves of the tail of a fish or whale; an internal parasitic flatworm, as the liver fluke of sheep

gaff, a strong, pointed hook

gaudy, showy, flashy, many-colored

gauge, to measure

gelatinous, jelly-like

235

genera, plural of *genus*, a division of the animal or plant kingdom between the *family* and the *species*

gill arches, the bony arches to which the gills of fishes are attached

gills, organs for breathing the air contained in water

gristle, cartilage; a substance harder than flesh and softer than bone

gullet, the food canal or duct extending from the mouth to the stomach

habitat, the kind of place where an animal or plant lives

herbivorous, eating plant food

heterocercal, said of the tail of fishes when the two halves or flukes are unequal in size

hibernate, to sleep throughout the winter in a torpid state

hibernation, the act of hibernating

hummock, a clump or hillock of earth or moss in a swamp or bog

iridescent, shining in changing rainbow colors

larval stage, an animal in an immature form, which must undergo a change to become adult, as the caterpillar is the larval stage of a butterfly or moth

laterally, sidewise

lave, wash

lethargy, unnatural drowsiness or prolonged sleep

ligature, anything that serves for binding or tying, as in tying off a blood vessel

literally, according to the letter

mandible, the lower jaw

marine, pertaining to or living in the ocean

meditation, the act of pondering or thinking over

membrane, a thin sheet-like or skin-like structure

membranous, pertaining to a membrane

mollusks, soft-bodied animals such as snails and clams

mosaic, inlaid work, usually consisting of small colored stones, laid in cement, and making a pattern or figure

myth, fairy tale

nasal, pertaining to the nose or to the nostrils

normal, usual, ordinary

omnivorous, eating all kinds of food; eating both plant and animal food

oviparous, producing eggs

palate, the roof of the mouth

pancreas, a gland emptying into the small intestine, the fluid from which turns starch into sugar

parotoid glands, glands behind the eyes of a toad which secrete or give off a sharp, biting, slightly poisonous fluid

pectoral, pertaining to the breast

pectoral fin, the first pair of fins of fishes, corresponding to the forelegs of higher animals

pelvic girdle, the basin-like part of the skeleton to which the legs are attached

pharyngeal, pertaining to the pharynx

pharynx, the rear part of the mouth

plastron, the under shell of a turtle

polluted, rendered impure

posterior, rear, toward the back

predacious, seeking living prey for food

preëminent, outstanding

prepossessing, good-looking; attractive

prodigious, enormous; wonderful; surprising

prolific, having many young

propagation, act of breeding, producing, or spreading

protein, nitrogenous material in animal or vegetable substances

pulmonary, pertaining to the lungs

quadrate, a bone or set of bones lying between the lower jaw and the skull, chiefly in snakes, which enables them greatly to extend the mouth vertically

rapacious, greedy for food, seizing it by violent means
rasp, file
reptiles, changeable-blooded, creeping or crawling, air-breathing vertebrates
respiration, the act of breathing; inhaling oxygen and exhaling carbon dioxide
rigidity, stiffness

scute, an external, horny plate or scale
serrated, notched like a saw
spawn, the eggs of amphibians and fishes, often deposited in coherent masses
spine, a sharp projecting point; a thorn

taxidermist, one who prepares and mounts the skins of animals
tenacious of life, hard to kill
torpid, sluggish, inactive
transverse scales, scales running crosswise, as those on the belly of snakes
tubercles, small outgrowths like pimples
tympanic, pertaining to the tympanum
tympanum, the membrane in the ear which makes hearing possible

variability, ability to change
venom, poison
vent, the external opening of the alimentary canal
ventricle, one of the thick-walled chambers of the heart
vertically, up and down
viviparous, bringing forth living young
voracious, greedy for food

wanton, reckless; unrestrained